The Institution of Civil Engineers

The Engineering and Construction Subcontract

An NEC document

Thomas Telford, London

Published for the Institution of Civil Engineers by Thomas Telford Services Ltd,
Thomas Telford House, 1 Heron Quay, London E14 4JD.

The NEC System is published as a series of documents of which this is one.

ISBN (series) 0 7277 2081 3

ISBN (this document) 0 7277 2078 3

Consultative edition 1991
First edition 1993
Second edition November 1995

British Library Cataloguing in Publication Data for this publication is available from the
British Library.

Printed and bound in Great Britain by Staples Printers Rochester Ltd, Rochester, Kent.

CONTENTS

ACKNOWLEDGEMENTS

The New Engineering Contract 1st edition was produced by the Institution of Civil Engineers through its New Engineering Contract Working Group.

The New Engineering Contract has been designed and drafted by Dr Martin Barnes of Coopers and Lybrand with the assistance of Professor J. G. Perry of The University of Birmingham, T. W. Weddell of Travers Morgan Management, T. H. Nicholson, Consultant to the Institution of Civil Engineers, A. Norman of the University of Manchester Institute of Science and Technology and P. A. Baird, Corporate Contracts Consultant, Eskom, South Africa.

The members of the New Engineering Contract Working Group were

    R. L. Wilson, CBE, BSc(Eng), FEng, FICE (Chairman)
    M. W. Abrahamson, BA, LLB, FCIArb
    P. A. Baird, BSc, CEng, FICE, M(SA)ICE, MAPM
    M. Barnes, BSc(Eng), PhD, FEng, FICE, FCIOB, CBIM, FAPM, FInstCES, ACIArb
    J. A. Chandler, MA, CEng, FICE, FCIArb
    L. T. Eames, BSc, FRICS, MCIOB
    F. Griffiths, CEng, FIEE, FICE, FCIPS, FInstM, MAPM
    J. Halliday, CEng, MICE
    K. Lumb, FRICS, ACIArb
    W. S. McAlonan, MSc, FEng, FICE, FIHT
    T. H. Nicholson, BSc, CEng, FICE (Secretary)
    A. Norman, BSc, MSc, CEng, MICE, MAPM
    Professor J. G. Perry, MEng, PhD, CEng, MICE, MAPM
    T. W. Weddell, BSc, CEng, DIC, FICE, FIStructE, ACIArb

    I. M. H. Moore, CBE (Director External Affairs, ICE)
    J. J. Lewis (Project Manager, June 1991 – January 1992)
    R. F. Bell, BSc, CEng, FICE (Project Manager from January 1992)

The Institution of Civil Engineers also acknowledges the considerable contributions made to the New Engineering Contract 1st edition by

    N. G. Bunni, BSc, MSc, PhD, CEng, FIEI, FICE, FCIArb
    S. C. McCarthy, BE, MSc, PhD, MIEI

The 2nd edition of the NEC documents for engineering and construction contracts were produced by the Institution of Civil Engineers through its New Engineering Contract Panel

The members of the New Engineering Contract Panel are:

    M. Barnes (Chairman), BSc(Eng), PhD, FEng, FICE, FCIOB, CIMgt, MBCS, FRSA, FAPM, FInstCES, ACIArb
    P. A. Baird, BSc, CEng, FICE, M(SA)ICE, MAPM
    L. T. Eames, BSc FRICS, MCIOB
    T. H. Nicholson (Secretary), BSc, CEng, FICE
    M. A. Noakes, BSc(Eng), CEng, MICE, MIWEM
    Professor J. G. Perry, MEng, PhD, CEng, FICE, MAPM
    N. C. Shaw, FCIPS, CEng, MIMechE
    T. W. Weddell, BSc, CEng, DIC, FICE, FIStructE, ACIArb

The Institution of Civil Engineers also acknowledges the help in preparing the second edition given by many other people and, in particular by:

J. C. Broome BEng
Professor P. N. Capper
G. C. Dixon MA
D. P. Maidment ACII
A. Norman, BSc, MSc, CEng, MICE, MAPM

SCHEDULE OF OPTIONS

The strategy for choosing the form of subcontract starts with a decision between five main options, one of which must be chosen.

Option A	Priced subcontract with activity schedule
Option B	Priced subcontract with bill of quantities
Option C	Target subcontract with activity schedule
Option D	Target subcontract with bill of quantities
Option E	Cost reimbursable subcontract

The following secondary options should then be considered. It is not necessary to use any of them. Any combination other than those stated may be used.

Option G	Performance bond
Option H	Parent company guarantee
Option J	Advanced payment to the *Subcontractor*
Option K	Multiple currencies (not to be used with Options C, D and E)
Option L	Sectional Completion
Option M	Limitation of the *Subcontractor*'s liability for his design to reasonable skill and care
Option N	Price adjustment for inflation (not to be used with Option E)
Option P	Retention
Option Q	Bonus for early Completion
Option R	Delay damages
Option S	Low performance damages
Option T	Changes in the law
Option U	The Construction (Design and Management) Regulations 1994 (to be used for contracts in the UK)
Option V	Trust Fund
Option Z	Additional conditions of subcontract

THE ENGINEERING AND CONSTRUCTION SUBCONTRACT

CORE CLAUSES

1. General

Actions	**10**
	10.1 The *Contractor* and the *Subcontractor* shall act as stated in this subcontract and in a spirit of mutual trust and co-operation. The *Adjudicator* shall act as stated in this subcontract and in a spirit of independence.
Identified and defined terms	**11**
	11.1 In these conditions of subcontract, terms identified in the Subcontract Data are in italics and defined terms have capital initials.
	11.2 (1) The Parties are the *Contractor* and the *Subcontractor*.

(2) Others are people or organisations who are not the *Employer*, the *Project Manager*, the *Supervisor*, the *Adjudicator*, the *Subcontractor*, the *Contractor* or any employee, Subsubcontractor or supplier of the *Subcontractor*.

(3) The Subcontract Date is the date when this subcontract came into existence.

(4) To Provide the Subcontract Works means to do the work necessary to complete the *subcontract works* in accordance with this subcontract and all incidental work, services and actions which this subcontract requires.

(5) Subcontract Works Information is information which either

- specifies and describes the *subcontract works* or
- states any constraints on how the *Subcontractor* Provides the Subcontract Works

and is either

- in the documents which the Subcontract Data states it is in or
- in an instruction given in accordance with this subcontract.

(6) Site Information is information which

- describes the Site and its surroundings and
- is in the documents which the Subcontract Data states it is in.

(7) The Site is the area within the *boundaries of the site* and the volumes above and below it which are affected by work included in this subcontract.

(8) The Working Areas are the *working areas* unless later changed in accordance with this subcontract.

(9) A Subsubcontractor is a person or corporate body who has a contract with the *Subcontractor* to provide part of the *subcontract works* or to supply Plant and Materials which he has wholly or partly designed specifically for the *subcontract works*.

(10) Plant and Materials are items intended to be included in the *subcontract works*.

(11) Equipment is items provided by the *Subcontractor* and used by him to Provide the Subcontract Works and which the Subcontract Works Information does not require him to include in the *subcontract works*.

(12) The Subcontract Completion Date is the *subcontract completion date* unless later changed in accordance with this subcontract.

(13) Completion is when the *Subcontractor* has

- done all the work which the Subcontract Works Information states he is to do by the Subcontract Completion Date and
- corrected notified Defects which would have prevented the *Contractor* or the *Employer* from using the *subcontract works*.

(14) The Accepted Programme is the programme identified in the Subcontract Data or is the latest programme accepted by the *Contractor*. The latest programme accepted by the *Contractor* supersedes previous Accepted Programmes.

(15) A Defect is

- a part of the *subcontract works* which is not completed in accordance with the Subcontract Works Information or
- a part of the *subcontract works* designed by the *Subcontractor*, which is not in accordance with

  - the applicable law or
  - the *Subcontractor*'s design which has been accepted by the *Contractor*.

(16) The Defects Certificate is either a list of Defects that the *Contractor* has notified before the *defects date* which the *Subcontractor* has not corrected or, if there are no such Defects, a statement that there are none.

(17) The Fee is the amount calculated by applying the *fee percentage* to the amount of Actual Cost.

Interpretation and the Law **12**

12.1 In this subcontract, except where the context shows otherwise, words in the singular also mean in the plural and the other way round and words in the masculine also mean in the feminine and neuter.

12.2 This subcontract is governed by the *law of the subcontract*.

Communications **13**

13.1 Each instruction, certificate, submission, proposal, record, acceptance, notification and reply which this subcontract requires is communicated in a form which can be read, copied and recorded. Writing is in the *language of this subcontract*.

13.2 A communication has effect when it is received at the last address notified by the recipient for receiving communications or, if none is notified, at the address of the recipient stated in the Subcontract Data.

13.3 If this subcontract requires the *Contractor* or the *Subcontractor* to reply to a communication, unless otherwise stated in this subcontract, he replies within the *period for reply*.

13.4 The *Contractor* replies to a communication submitted or resubmitted to him by the *Subcontractor* for acceptance. If his reply is not acceptance, he states his reasons and the *Subcontractor* resubmits the communication within the *period for reply* taking account of these reasons. A reason for witholding acceptance is that more information is needed in order to assess the *Subcontractor*'s submission fully.

13.5   The *Contractor* may extend the *period for reply* to a communication if the *Contractor* and the *Subcontractor* agree to the extension before the reply is due. The *Contractor* notifies the extension which has been agreed to the *Subcontractor*.

13.6   The *Contractor* issues his certificates to the *Subcontractor*.

13.7   A notification which this subcontract requires is communicated separately from other communications.

13.8   The *Contractor* may withold acceptance of a submission by the *Subcontractor*. Witholding acceptance for a reason stated in this subcontract is not a compensation event.

The *Contractor* 14

14.1   The *Contractor*'s acceptance of a communication from the *Subcontractor* or of his work does not change the *Subcontractor*'s responsibility to Provide the Subcontract Works or his liability for his design.

14.2   The *Contractor*, after notifying the *Subcontractor*, may delegate any of his actions and may cancel any delegation. A reference to an action of the *Contractor* in this subcontract includes an action by his delegate.

14.3   The *Contractor* may give an instruction to the *Subcontractor* which changes the Subcontract Works Information.

**Adding to the *working* 15
*areas***

15.1   The *Subcontractor* may submit a proposal for adding to the Working Areas to the *Contractor* for acceptance. A reason for not accepting is that

- the proposed addition is not necessary for Providing the Subcontract Works or
- the proposed area will be used for work not in this subcontract.

Early warning 16

16.1   The *Subcontractor* and the *Contractor* give an early warning by notifying the other as soon as either becomes aware of any matter which

- could increase the total of the Prices,
- delay Completion or
- impair the performance of the *subcontract works* in use.

16.2   Either the *Contractor* or the *Subcontractor* may instruct the other to attend an early warning meeting. Each may instruct other people to attend if the other agrees.

16.3   At an early warning meeting, those who attend co-operate in

- making and considering proposals for how the effect of each matter which has been notified as an early warning can be avoided or reduced,
- seeking solutions that will bring advantage to all those who will be affected and
- deciding upon actions which they will take and who, in accordance with this subcontract, will take them.

16.4   The *Contractor* records the proposals considered and the decisions taken at an early warning meeting and gives a copy of his record to the *Subcontractor*.

**Ambiguities and 17
inconsistencies**

17.1   The *Contractor* or the *Subcontractor* notifies the other as soon as either becomes aware of an ambiguity or inconsistency in or between the documents which are part of this subcontract. The *Contractor* gives an instruction resolving the ambiguity or inconsistency.

Health and safety	**18**	
	18.1	The *Subcontractor* acts in accordance with the health and safety requirements stated in the Subcontract Works Information.
Illegal and impossible requirements	**19**	
	19.1	The *Subcontractor* notifies the *Contractor* as soon as he becomes aware that the Subcontract Works Information requires him to do anything which is illegal or impossible. If the *Contractor* agrees, he gives an instruction to change the Subcontract Works Information appropriately.

2 The *Subcontractor*'s main responsibilities

Providing the Subcontract **20**
Works 20.1   The *Subcontractor* Provides the Subcontract Works in accordance with the Subcontract Works Information.

The *Subcontractor*'s **21**
design 21.1   The *Subcontractor* designs the parts of the *subcontract works* which the Subcontract Works Information states he is to design.

21.2   The *Subcontractor* submits the particulars of his design as the Subcontract Works Information requires to the *Contractor* for acceptance. A reason for not accepting the *Subcontractor*'s design is that

- it does not comply with the Subcontract Works Information or
- it does not comply with the applicable law.

The *Subcontractor* does not proceed with the relevant work until the *Contractor* has accepted his design.

21.3   The *Subcontractor* may submit his design for acceptance in parts if the design of each part can be assessed fully.

21.4   The *Subcontractor* indemnifies the *Contractor* and the *Employer* against claims, compensation and costs due to the *Subcontractor* infringing a patent or copyright.

21.5   The *Subcontractor*'s liability to the *Contractor* for Defects due to his design that are not listed on the Defects Certificate is limited to the amount stated in the Subcontract Data in addition to any damages stated in this subcontract for delay or low performance.

Using the *Subcontractor*'s **22**
design 22.1   The *Employer* and the *Contractor* may use and copy the *Subcontractor*'s design for any purpose, connected with construction, use, alteration or demolition of the *subcontract works* unless otherwise stated in the Subcontract Works Information and for other purposes as stated in the Subcontract Works Information.

Design of Subcontract **23**
Equipment 23.1   The *Subcontractor* submits particulars of the design of an item of Equipment to the *Contractor* for acceptance if the *Contractor* instructs him to. A reason for not accepting is that the design of the item will not allow the *Subcontractor* to Provide the Subcontract Works in accordance with

- the Subcontract Works Information,
- the *Subcontractor*'s design which the *Contractor* has accepted or
- the applicable law.

People **24**
24.1   The *Subcontractor* either employs each key person named to do the job for him stated in the Subcontract Data or employs a replacement person who has been accepted by the *Contractor*. The *Subcontractor* submits the name, relevant qualifications and experience of a proposed replacement person to the *Contractor* for acceptance. A reason for not accepting the person is that his relevant qualifications and experience are not as good as those of the person who is to be replaced.

24.2   The *Contractor* may, having stated his reasons, instruct the *Subcontractor* to remove an employee. The *Subcontractor* then arranges that, after one day, the employee has no further connection with the work included in this subcontract.

Co-operation **25**

25.1 The *Subcontractor* co-operates with Others in obtaining and providing information which they need in connection with the *subcontract works*. He shares the Working Areas with Others as stated in the Subcontract Works Information.

Subsubcontracting **26**

26.1 If the *Subcontractor* subsubcontracts work, he is responsible for performing this subcontract as if he had not subsubcontracted. This subcontract applies as if a Subsubcontractor's employees and equipment were the *Subcontractor*'s.

26.2 The *Subcontractor* submits the name of each proposed Subsubcontractor to the *Contractor* for acceptance. A reason for not accepting the Subsubcontractor is that his appointment will not allow the *Subcontractor* to Provide the Subcontract Works. The *Subcontractor* does not appoint a proposed Subsubcontractor until the *Contractor* has accepted him.

26.3 The *Subcontractor* submits the proposed conditions of contract for each subsubcontract to the *Contractor* for acceptance unless

- the NEC Engineering and Construction Subcontract or the NEC Professional Services Contract is to be used or
- the *Contractor* has agreed that no submission is required.

The *Subcontractor* does not appoint a Subsubcontractor on the proposed subsubcontract conditions submitted until the *Contractor* has accepted them. A reason for not accepting them is that

- they will not allow the *Subcontractor* to Provide the Subcontract Works or
- they do not include a statement that the parties to the subsubcontract shall act in a spirit of mutual trust and co-operation.

Approval from Others **27**

27.1 The *Subcontractor* obtains approval of his design from Others where necessary.

Access to the work **28**

28.1 The *Subcontractor* provides access to work being done and to Plant and Materials being stored for this subcontract for

- the *Contractor*
- the *Project Manager*
- the *Supervisor*
- others notified to him by the *Contractor* or the *Project Manager*.

Instructions **29**

29.1 The *Subcontractor* obeys an instruction which is in accordance with this subcontract and is given to him by the *Contractor*.

3 Time

Starting and Completion **30**

30.1 The *Subcontractor* does not start work on the Site until the first *subcontract possession date* and does the work so that Completion is on or before the Subcontract Completion Date.

30.2 The *Contractor* decides the date of Completion. The *Contractor* certifies Completion within two weeks of Completion.

The programme **31**

31.1 If a programme is not identified in the Subcontract Data, the *Subcontractor* submits a first programme to the *Contractor* for acceptance within the period stated in the Subcontract Data.

31.2 The *Subcontractor* shows on each programme which he submits for acceptance

- the *subcontract starting date*, *subcontract possession dates* and Subcontract Completion Date,
- for each operation, a method statement which identifies the Equipment and other resources which the *Subcontractor* plans to use,
- planned Completion,
- the order and timing of

    - the operations which the *Subcontractor* plans to do in order to Provide the Subcontract Works and
    - the work of the *Employer*, the *Contractor* and Others either as stated in the Subcontract Works Information or as later agreed with them by the *Subcontractor*,

- the dates when the *Subcontractor* plans to complete work needed to allow the *Employer*, the *Contractor* or Others to do their work,
- provisions for

    - float
    - time risk allowances
    - health and safety requirements
    - the procedures set out in this subcontract

- the dates when, in order to Provide the Subcontract Works in accordance with his programme, the *Subcontractor* will need

    - possession of a part of the Site if later than its *subcontract possession date*,
    - acceptances and
    - Plant and Materials and other things to be provided by the *Employer* and the *Contractor* and

- other information which the Subcontract Works Information requires the *Subcontractor* to show on a programme submitted for acceptance.

31.3 Within two weeks of the *Subcontractor* submitting a programme to him for acceptance, the *Contractor* either accepts the programme or notifies the *Subcontractor* of his reasons for not accepting it. A reason for not accepting a programme is that

- the *Subcontractor*'s plans which it shows are not practicable,
- it does not show the information which this subcontract requires,
- it does not represent the *Subcontractor*'s plans realistically or
- it does not comply with the Subcontract Works Information.

Revising the programme **32**

32.1 The *Subcontractor* shows on each revised programme

- the actual progress achieved on each operation and its effect upon the timing of the remaining work,
- the effects of implemented compensation events and of notified early warning matters,
- how the *Subcontractor* plans to deal with any delays and to correct notified Defects and
- any other changes which the *Subcontractor* proposes to make to the Accepted Programme.

32.2 The *Subcontractor* submits a revised programme to the *Contractor* for acceptance

- within the *period for reply* after the *Contractor* has instructed him to,
- when the *Subcontractor* chooses to and, in any case,
- at no longer interval than the interval stated in the Subcontract Data from the *subcontract starting date* until Completion of the whole of the *subcontract works*.

Possession of the Site **33**

33.1 The *Contractor* gives possession of each part of the Site to the *Subcontractor* on or before the later of its *subcontract possession date* and the date for possession shown on the Accepted Programme.

33.2 While the *Subcontractor* has possession of a part of the Site, the *Contractor* gives the *Subcontractor* access to and use of it and the *Contractor* and the *Subcontractor* provide facilities and services as stated in the Subcontract Works Information. Any cost incurred by the *Contractor* as a result of the *Subcontractor* not providing the facilities and services he is to provide is assessed by the *Contractor* and paid by the *Subcontractor*.

Instructions to stop or not **34**
to start work 34.1 The *Contractor* may instruct the *Subcontractor* to stop or not to start any work and may later instruct him that he may re-start or start it.

Take over **35**

35.1 Possession of each part of the Site returns to the *Contractor* when he takes over the part of the *subcontract works* which occupies it. Possession of the whole Site returns to the *Contractor* when the *Contractor* certifies termination.

35.2 The *Contractor* need not take over the *subcontract works* before the Subcontract Completion Date if it is stated in the Subcontract Data that he is not willing to do so. Otherwise the *Contractor* takes over the *subcontract works* not more than two weeks after Completion.

35.3 The *Employer* may use any part of the *subcontract works* before Completion has been certified. If he does so, the *Contractor* takes over the part of the *subcontract works* when the *Employer* begins to use it except if the use is

- for a reason stated in the Subcontract Works Information or
- to suit the *Subcontractor*'s method of working.

35.4 The *Contractor* certifies the date upon which he takes over any part of the *subcontract works* and its extent within two weeks of the date.

Acceleration 36

36.1 The *Contractor* may instruct the *Subcontractor* to submit a quotation for an acceleration to achieve Completion before the Subcontract Completion Date. A quotation for an acceleration comprises proposed changes to the Prices and the Subcontract Completion Date and a revised programme.

36.2 The *Subcontractor* submits a quotation or gives his reasons for not doing so within the *period for reply*.

4 Testing and Defects

Tests and inspections	**40**	
	40.1	This clause only governs tests and inspections required by the Subcontract Works Information and the applicable law.

40.2 The *Subcontractor*, the *Contractor* and the *Employer* provide materials, facilities and samples for tests and inspections as stated in the Subcontract Works Information.

40.3 The *Subcontractor* and the *Contractor* each notifies the other of each of his tests and inspections before it starts and afterwards notifies the other of its results. The *Subcontractor* notifies the *Contractor* in time for a test or inspection to be arranged and done before doing work which would obstruct the test or inspection. The *Contractor* and the *Supervisor* may watch any test done by the *Subcontractor*.

40.4 If a test or inspection shows that any work has a Defect, the *Subcontractor* corrects the Defect and the test or inspection is repeated.

40.5 The *Contractor* does his tests and inspections without causing unnecessary delay to the work or to a payment which is conditional upon a test or inspection being successful. A payment which is conditional upon a *Contractor*'s or *Supervisor*'s test or inspection being successful becomes due at the later of the *defects date* and the end of the last *defect correction period* if

- the *Contractor* or the *Supervisor* has not done the test or inspection and
- the delay to the test or inspection is not the *Subcontractor*'s fault.

40.6 The *Contractor* assesses the cost incurred by him in repeating a test or inspection after a Defect is found. The *Subcontractor* pays the amount assessed.

Testing and inspection before delivery **41**

41.1 The *Subcontractor* does not bring to the Working Areas those Plant and Materials which the Subcontract Works Information states are to be tested or inspected before delivery until the *Contractor* has notified the *Subcontractor* that they have passed the test or inspection.

Searching and notifying Defects **42**

42.1 The *Contractor* may instruct the *Subcontractor* to search. He gives his reason for the search with his instruction. Searching may include

- uncovering, dismantling, re-covering and re-erecting work,
- providing facilities, materials and samples for tests and inspections done by the *Contractor* or the *Supervisor* and
- doing tests and inspections which the Subcontract Works Information does not require.

42.2 Until the *defects date*, the *Contractor* notifies the *Subcontractor* of each Defect which he finds and the *Subcontractor* notifies the *Contractor* of each Defect which he finds.

Correcting Defects **43**

43.1 The *Subcontractor* corrects Defects whether or not the *Contractor* notifies him of them. The *Subcontractor* corrects notified Defects before the end of the *defect correction period*. This period begins at Completion for Defects notified before Completion and when the Defect is notified for other Defects.

43.2 The *Contractor* issues the Defects Certificate at the later of the *defects date* and the end of the last *defect correction period*.

43.3 The *Contractor* makes arrangements to give to the *Subcontractor* access to and use of any part of the *subcontract works* which he has taken over if it is needed for correcting a Defect. If the *Contractor* has not arranged suitable access and use within the *defect correction period*, he extends the period for correcting the Defect as necessary.

Accepting Defects 44

44.1 The *Subcontractor* and the *Contractor* may each propose to the other that the Subcontract Works Information should be changed so that a Defect does not have to be corrected.

44.2 If the *Subcontractor* and the *Contractor* are prepared to consider the change, the *Subcontractor* submits a quotation for reduced Prices or an earlier Subcontract Completion Date or both to the *Contractor* for acceptance. If the *Contractor* accepts the quotation, he gives an instruction to change the Subcontract Works Information, the Prices and the Subcontract Completion Date accordingly.

Uncorrected Defects 45

45.1 If the *Subcontractor* has not corrected a notified Defect within its *defect correction period*, the *Contractor* assesses the cost of having the Defect corrected by other people and the *Subcontractor* pays this amount.

5 Payment

Assessing the amount due   **50**

50.1   The *Contractor* assesses the amount due at each assessment date. The first assessment date is decided by the *Contractor* to suit the procedures of the Parties and is not later than the *assessment interval* after the *subcontract starting date*. Later assessment dates occur

- at the end of each *assessment interval* until Completion of the whole of the *subcontract works*,
- at Completion of the whole of the *subcontract works*,
- four weeks after the *Contractor* issues the Defects Certificate and
- after Completion of the whole of the *subcontract works*

  - when an amount due is corrected and
  - when a payment is made late.

50.2   The amount due is the Price for Work Done to Date plus other amounts to be paid to the *Subcontractor* less amounts to be paid by or retained from the *Subcontractor*. Any value added tax or sales tax which the law requires the *Contractor* to pay to the *Subcontractor* is included in the amount due.

50.3   If no programme is identified in the Subcontract Data, one quarter of the Price for Work Done to Date is retained in assessments of the amount due until the *Subcontractor* has submitted a first programme to the *Contractor* for acceptance showing the information which this subcontract requires.

50.4   In assessing the amount due, the *Contractor* considers any application for payment the *Subcontractor* has submitted on or before the assessment date. The *Contractor* gives the *Subcontractor* details of how the amount due has been assessed.

50.5   The *Contractor* corrects any wrongly assessed amount due in a later payment certificate.

Payment   **51**

51.1   The *Contractor* certifies a payment within two weeks of each assessment date. The first payment is the amount due. Other payments are the change in the amount due since the last payment certificate. A payment is made by the *Subcontractor* to the *Contractor* if the change reduces the amount due. Other payments are made by the *Contractor* to the *Subcontractor*. Payments are in the *currency of this subcontract* unless otherwise stated in this subcontract.

51.2   Each certified payment is made within four weeks of the assessment date or, if a different period is stated in the Subcontract Data, within the period stated. If a payment is late, interest is paid on the late payment. Interest is assessed from the date by which the late payment should have been made until the date when the late payment is made, and is included in the first assessment after the late payment is made.

51.3   If an amount due is corrected in a later certificate either

- by the *Contractor*, whether in relation to a mistake or a compensation event, or
- following a decision of the *Adjudicator* or the *tribunal*,

interest on the correcting amount is paid. Interest is assessed from the date when the incorrect amount was certified until the date when the correcting amount is certified, and is included in the assessment which includes the correcting amount.

51.4   If the *Contractor* does not issue a certificate which he should issue, interest is paid on the amount which he should have certified. Interest is assessed from the date by which he should have certified the amount until the date when he certifies the amount and it is included in the amount then certified.

51.5   Interest is calculated at the *interest rate* and is compounded annually.

Actual Cost **52**

52.1   All the *Subcontractor*'s costs which are not included in Actual Cost are deemed to be included in the *fee percentage*. Amounts included in Actual Cost are at open market or competitively tendered prices with all discounts, rebates and taxes which can be recovered deducted.

6 Compensation events

Compensation events   **60**

60.1   The following are compensation events.

(1) The *Contractor* gives an instruction changing the Subcontract Works Information except

- a change made in order to accept a Defect or
- a change to the Subcontract Works Information provided by the *Subcontractor* for his design which is made at his request or to comply with Subcontract Works Information provided by the *Contractor*.

(2) The *Contractor* does not give possession of a part of the Site by the later of its *subcontract possession date* and the date required by the Accepted Programme.

(3) The *Contractor* does not provide something which he is to provide by the date for providing it required by the Accepted Programme.

(4) The *Contractor* gives an instruction to stop or not to start any work.

(5) The *Employer*, the *Contractor* or Others do not work within the times shown on the Accepted Programme or do not work within the conditions stated in the Subcontract Works Information.

(6) The *Contractor* does not reply to a communication from the *Subcontractor* within the period required by this contract.

(7) The *Contractor* gives an instruction for dealing with an object of value or of historical or other interest found within the Site.

(8) The *Contractor* changes a decision which he has previously communicated to the *Subcontractor*.

(9) The *Contractor* withholds an acceptance (other than acceptance of a quotation for acceleration or for not correcting a Defect) for a reason not stated in this subcontract.

(10) The *Contractor* instructs the *Subcontractor* to search and no Defect is found unless the search is needed only because the *Subcontractor* gave insufficient notice of doing work obstructing a required test or inspection.

(11) A test or inspection done by the *Contractor* or the *Supervisor* causes unnecessary delay.

(12) The *Subcontractor* encounters physical conditions which

- are within the Site,
- are not weather conditions and
- which an experienced subcontractor would have judged at the Subcontract Date to have such a small chance of occurring that it would have been unreasonable for him to have allowed for them.

(13) A *weather measurement* is recorded

- within a calendar month,
- before the Subcontract Completion Date for the whole of the *subcontract works* and
- at the place stated in the Subcontract Data

the value of which, by comparison with the *weather data*, is shown to occur on average less frequently than once in ten years.

(14) An *Employer*'s or *Contractor*'s risk event occurs.

(15) The *Contractor* certifies take over of a part of the *subcontract works* before both Completion and the Subcontract Completion Date.

(16) The *Contractor* or the *Employer* does not provide materials, facilities and samples for tests as stated in the Subcontract Works Information.

(17) The *Contractor* notifies a correction to an assumption about the nature of a compensation event.

(18) A breach of contract by the *Contractor* which is not one of the compensation events in this subcontract.

60.2 In judging the expected physical conditions, the *Subcontractor* is assumed to have taken into account

- the Site Information,
- publicly available information referred to in the Site Information,
- information obtainable from a visual inspection of the Site and
- other information which an experienced subcontractor could reasonably be expected to have or to obtain.

60.3 If there is an inconsistency within the Site Information (including the information referred to in it), the *Subcontractor* is assumed to have taken into account the physical conditions more favourable to doing the work.

Notifying compensation events **61**

61.1 For compensation events which arise from the *Contractor* giving an instruction or changing an earlier decision, the *Contractor* notifies the *Subcontractor* of the compensation event at the time of the event. He also instructs the *Subcontractor* to submit quotations, unless the event arises from a fault of the *Subcontractor* or quotations have already been submitted. The *Subcontractor* puts the instruction or changed decision into effect.

61.2 The *Contractor* may instruct the *Subcontractor* to submit quotations for a proposed instruction or a proposed changed decision. The *Subcontractor* does not put a proposed instruction or a proposed changed decision into effect.

61.3 The *Subcontractor* notifies an event which has happened or which he expects to happen to the *Contractor* as a compensation event if

- the *Subcontractor* believes that the event is a compensation event,
- it is less than one week since he became aware of the event and
- the *Contractor* has not notified the event to the *Subcontractor*.

61.4 The Prices and the Subcontract Completion Date are not changed if the *Contractor* decides that an event notified by the *Subcontractor*

- arises from a fault of the *Subcontractor*,
- has not happened or is not expected to happen,
- has no effect upon Actual Cost or Completion or
- is not one of the compensation events stated in this subcontract.

If the *Contractor* decides otherwise, he instructs the *Subcontractor* to submit quotations for the event. Within either

- one week of the *Subcontractor*'s notification or
- a longer period to which the *Subcontractor* has agreed

the *Contractor* notifies his decision to the *Subcontractor* or instructs him to submit quotations.

61.5   If the *Contractor* decides that the *Subcontractor* did not give an early warning of the event which an experienced subcontractor could have given, he notifies this decision to the *Subcontractor* when he instructs him to submit quotations.

61.6   If the *Contractor* decides that the effects of a compensation event are too uncertain to be forecast reasonably, he states assumptions about the event in his instruction to the *Subcontractor* to submit quotations. Assessment of the event is based on these assumptions. If any of them is later found to have been wrong, the *Contractor* notifies a correction.

61.7   A compensation event is not notified after the *defects date*.

Quotations for compensation events   **62**

62.1   The *Contractor* may instruct the *Subcontractor* to submit alternative quotations based upon different ways of dealing with the compensation event which are practicable. The *Subcontractor* submits the required quotations to the *Contractor* and may submit quotations for other methods of dealing with the compensation event which he considers practicable.

62.2   Quotations for compensation events comprise proposed changes to the Prices and any delay to the Subcontract Completion Date assessed by the *Subcontractor*. The *Subcontractor* submits details of his assessment with each quotation. If the programme for remaining work is affected by the compensation event, the *Subcontractor* includes a revised programme in his quotation showing the effect.

62.3   The *Subcontractor* submits quotations within one week of being instructed to do so by the *Contractor*. The *Contractor* replies within four weeks of the submission. His reply is

- an instruction to submit a revised quotation,
- an acceptance of a quotation,
- a notification that a proposed instruction or a proposed changed decision will not be given or
- a notification that he will be making his own assessment.

62.4   The *Contractor* instructs the *Subcontractor* to submit a revised quotation only after explaining his reasons for doing so to the *Subcontractor*. The *Subcontractor* submits the revised quotation within one week of being instructed to do so.

62.5   The *Contractor* extends the time allowed for

- the *Subcontractor* to submit quotations for a compensation event and
- the *Contractor* to reply to a quotation

if the *Contractor* and the *Subcontractor* agree to the extension before the submission or reply is due. The *Contractor* notifies the extension that has been agreed to the *Subcontractor*.

Assessing compensation events   **63**

63.1   The changes to the Prices are assessed as the effect of the compensation event upon

- the Actual Cost of the work already done,
- the forecast Actual Cost of the work not yet done and
- the resulting Fee.

63.2   If the effect of a compensation event is to reduce the total Actual Cost, the Prices are not reduced except as stated in this subcontract. If the effect of a compensation event is to reduce the total Actual Cost, and the event is

- a change to the Subcontract Works Information or
- a correction of an assumption stated by the *Contractor* for assessing an earlier compensation event,

the Prices are reduced.

63.3   A delay to the Subcontract Completion Date is assessed as the length of time that, due to the compensation event, planned Completion is later than planned Completion as shown on the Accepted Programme.

63.4   If the *Contractor* has notified the *Subcontractor* of his decision that the *Subcontractor* did not give an early warning of a compensation event which an experienced subcontractor could have given, the event is assessed as if the *Subcontractor* had given early warning.

63.5   Assessment of the effect of a compensation event includes cost and time risk allowances for matters which have a significant chance of occurring and are at the *Subcontractor*'s risk under this subcontract.

63.6   Assessments are based upon the assumptions that the *Subcontractor* reacts competently and promptly to the compensation event, that the additional Actual Cost and time due to the event are reasonably incurred and that the Accepted Programme can be changed.

63.7   A compensation event which is an instruction to change the Subcontract Works Information in order to resolve an ambiguity or inconsistency is assessed as follows. If Subcontract Works Information provided by the *Contractor* is changed, the effect of the compensation event is assessed as if the Prices and the Subcontract Completion Date were for the interpretation most favourable to the *Subcontractor*. If Subcontract Works Information provided by the *Subcontractor* is changed, the effect of the compensation event is assessed as if the Prices and the Subcontract Completion Date were for the interpretation most favourable to the *Contractor*.

The *Contractor*'s **64**
assessments 64.1   The *Contractor* assesses a compensation event

- if the *Subcontractor* has not submitted a required quotation and details of his assessment within the time allowed,
- if the *Contractor* decides that the *Subcontractor* has not assessed the compensation event correctly in a quotation and he does not instruct the *Subcontractor* to submit a revised quotation,
- if, when the *Subcontractor* submits quotations for a compensation event, he has not submitted a programme which this subcontract requires him to submit or
- if, when the *Subcontractor* submits quotations for a compensation event, the *Contractor* has not accepted the *Subcontractor*'s latest programme for one of the reasons stated in this subcontract.

64.2   The *Contractor* assesses a compensation event using his own assessment of the programme for the remaining work if

- there is no Accepted Programme or
- the *Subcontractor* has not submitted a revised programme for acceptance as required by this subcontract.

64.3 The *Contractor* notifies the *Subcontractor* of his assessment of a compensation event and gives him details of it within the period allowed for the *Subcontractor*'s submission of his quotation for the same event. This period starts when the need for the *Contractor*'s assessment becomes apparent.

Implementing 65
compensation events 65.1 The *Contractor* implements each compensation event by notifying the *Subcontractor* of the quotation which he has accepted or of his own assessment. He implements the compensation event when he accepts a quotation or completes his own assessment or when the compensation event occurs, whichever is latest.

65.2 The assessment of a compensation event is not revised if a forecast upon which it is based is shown by later recorded information to have been wrong.

7 Title

The *Contractor*'s title to Equipment, Plant and Materials   **70**

70.1   Whatever title the *Subcontractor* has to Equipment, Plant and Materials which is outside the Working Areas passes to the *Contractor* if the *Contractor* has marked it as for this subcontract.

70.2   Whatever title the *Subcontractor* has to Equipment, Plant and Materials passes to the *Contractor* if it has been brought within the Working Areas. The title to Equipment, Plant and Materials passes back to the *Subcontractor* if it is removed from the Working Areas with the *Contractor*'s permission.

Marking Equipment, Plant and Materials outside the Working Areas   **71**

71.1   The *Contractor* marks Equipment, Plant and Materials which are outside the Working Areas if

- this subcontract identifies them for payment and
- the *Subcontractor* has prepared them for marking as the Subcontract Works Information requires.

Removing Equipment   **72**

72.1   The *Subcontractor* removes Equipment from the Site when it is no longer needed unless the *Contractor* allows it to be left in the *subcontract works*.

Objects and materials found within the Site   **73**

73.1   The *Subcontractor* has no title to an object of value or of historical or other interest found within the Site. The *Subcontractor* notifies the *Contractor* when such an object is found and the *Contractor* instructs the *Subcontractor* how to deal with it. The *Subcontractor* does not move the object without instructions.

73.2   The *Subcontractor* has title to materials from excavation and demolition only as stated in the Subcontract Works Information.

8 Risks and insurance

The *Employer*'s and *Contractor*'s risks	**80**	
	80.1	The *Employer*'s and *Contractor*'s risks are

- Claims, proceedings, compensation and costs payable which are due to

  - use or occupation of the Site by the *works* or for the purpose of the *works* which is the unavoidable result of the *works*,
  - negligence, breach of statutory duty or interference with any legal right by the *Employer* or the *Contractor* or by any person employed by or contracted to them except the *Subcontractor* or

  - a fault of the *Employer* or *Contractor* or a fault in their designs.

- Loss of or damage to Plant and Materials supplied to the *Subcontractor* by the *Employer* or *Contractor* or by Others on the *Employer*'s or *Contractor*'s behalf, until the *Subcontractor* has received and accepted them.
- Loss of or damage to the *works*, Plant and Materials due to

  - war, civil war, rebellion, revolution, insurrection, military or usurped power,
  - strikes, riots and civil commotion not confined to the *Subcontractor*'s employees,
  - radioactive contamination.

- Loss of or damage to the parts of the *subcontract works* taken over by the *Employer* or *Contractor*, except loss or damage occurring before the issue of the Defects Certificate which is due to

  - Defect which existed at take over,
  - an event occurring before take over which was not itself an *Employer*'s or *Contractor*'s risk or
  - the activities of the *Subcontractor* on the Site after take over.

- Loss of or damage to the *subcontract works* and any Equipment, Plant and Materials retained on the Site by the *Employer* or *Contractor* after a termination, except loss and damage due to the activities of the *Subcontractor* on the Site after the termination.
- Additional *Employer*'s or *Contractor*'s risks stated in the Subcontract Data.

The *Subcontractor*'s risks	**81**	
	81.1	From the *subcontract starting date* until the Defects Certificate has been issued, the risks which are not carried by the *Employer* or the *Contractor* are carried by the *Subcontractor*.
Repairs	**82**	
	82.1	Unless the Defects Certificate has been issued and unless otherwise instructed by the *Contractor* the *Subcontractor* promptly replaces loss of and repairs damage to the *subcontract works*, Plant and Materials.
Indemnity	**83**	
	83.1	Each Party indemnifies the other against claims, proceedings, compensation and costs due to an event which is at his risk. The *Contractor* indemnifies the *Subcontractor* against all claims and liabilities against which the *Employer* idemnifies the *Contractor* under the main contract.

83.2 The liability of the *Subcontractor* to indemnify the *Contractor* is reduced if events at the *Employer*'s or *Contractor*'s risk contributed to the claims, proceedings, compensation and costs. The reduction is in proportion to the extent that events which were at the *Employer*'s or *Contractor*'s risk contributed, taking into account the responsibilities of each Party under this subcontract.

83.3 The liability of the *Contractor* to indemnify the *Subcontractor* is reduced if events at the *Subcontractor*'s risk contributed to the claims, proceedings, compensation and costs. The reduction is in proportion to the extent that events which were at the *Subcontractor*'s risk contributed, taking into account the responsibilities of each Party under this subcontract.

Insurance cover 84
84.1 The *Subcontractor* provides the insurances stated in the Insurance Table except any insurance which the *Employer* or the *Contractor* is to provide as stated in the Subcontract Data. The *Contractor* provides additional insurances as stated in the Subcontract Data.

84.2 The insurances are in the joint names of the Parties and provide cover for events which are at the *Subcontractor*'s risk from the *subcontract starting date* until the Defects Certificate has been issued.

INSURANCE TABLE

Insurance against	Minimum amount of cover or minimum limit of indemnity
Loss of or damage to the *subcontract works,* Plant and Materials.	The replacement cost, including the amount stated in the Subcontract Data for the replacement of any Plant and Materials provided by the *Employer* or *Contractor*.
Loss of or damage to Equipment.	The replacement cost.
Liability for loss of or damage to property (except the *subcontract works*, Plant and Materials and Equipment) and liability for bodily injury to or death of a person (not an employee of the *Subcontractor*) caused by activity in connection with this subcontract.	The amount stated in the Subcontract Data for any one event with cross liability so that the insurance applies to the Parties separately.
Liability for death of or bodily injury to employees of the *Subcontractor* arising out of and in the course of their employment in connection with this subcontract.	The greater of the amount required by the applicable law and the amount stated in the Subcontract Data for any one event.

Insurance policies 85
85.1 The *Subcontractor* submits policies and certificates for the insurance which he is to provide to the *Contractor* for acceptance before the *subcontract starting date* and afterwards as the *Contractor* instructs. A reason for not accepting the policies and certificates is that they do not comply with this subcontract.

85.2 Insurance policies include a waiver by the insurers of their subrogation rights against directors and other employees of every insured except where there is fraud.

	85.3	The Parties comply with the terms and conditions of the insurance policies.

85.4   Any amount not recovered from an insurer is borne by the *Employer* or *Contractor* for events which are at their risk, and by the *Subcontractor* for events which are at his risk.

If the *Subcontractor* does not insure   **86**

86.1   The *Contractor* may insure a risk which this subcontract requires the *Subcontractor* to insure if the *Subcontractor* does not submit a required policy or certificate. The cost of this insurance to the *Contractor* is paid by the *Subcontractor*.

Insurance by the *Employer* or the *Contractor*   **87**

87.1   The *Contractor* submits policies and certificates for insurances provided by the *Employer* or the *Contractor* to the *Subcontractor* for acceptance before the *subcontract starting date* and afterwards as the *Subcontractor* instructs. The *Subcontractor* accepts the policies and certificates if they comply with this subcontract.

87.2   The *Subcontractor*'s acceptance of an insurance policy or certificate provided by the *Employer* or *Contractor* does not change the responsibility of the *Employer* or *Contractor* to provide the insurances stated in the Subcontract Data.

87.3   The *Subcontractor* may insure a risk which this contract requires the *Employer* or *Contractor* to insure if the *Contractor* does not submit a required policy or certificate. The cost of this insurance to the *Subcontractor* is paid by the *Contractor*.

9 Disputes and termination

Settlement of disputes **90**

90.1 Any dispute arising under or in connection with this subcontract is submitted to and settled by the *Adjudicator* as follows

ADJUDICATION TABLE

Dispute about:	Which Party may submit it to the *Adjudicator*?	When may it be submitted to the *Adjudicator*?
An action of the *Contractor*	The *Subcontractor*	Between two and four weeks after the *Subcontractor*'s notification of the dispute to the *Contractor*, the notification itself being made not more than three weeks after the *Subcontractor* becomes aware of the action.
The *Contractor* not having taken an action	The *Subcontractor*	Between two and four weeks after the *Subcontractor*'s notification of the dispute to the *Contractor*, the notification itself being made not more than three weeks after the *Subcontractor* becomes aware that the action was not taken.
Any other matter	Either Party	Between two and four weeks after notification of the dispute to the other Party.

90.2 The *Adjudicator* settles the dispute by notifying the Parties of his decision, together with his reasons, within the time allowed by this subcontract. Unless and until there is such a settlement, the Parties proceed as if the action, inaction or other matter disputed were not disputed. The decision is final and binding unless and until revised by the *tribunal*.

The adjudication **91**

91.1 The Party submitting the dispute to the *Adjudicator* includes with his submission information to be considered by the *Adjudicator*. Any further information from a Party to be considered by the *Adjudicator* is provided within four weeks from the submission. The *Adjudicator* notifies his decision within four weeks of the end of the period for providing information. The four week periods in this clause may be extended if requested by the *Adjudicator* in view of the nature of the dispute and agreed by the Parties.

91.2 If a matter disputed under or in connection with a subsubcontract is also a matter disputed under or in connection with this subcontract, the *Subcontractor* may submit the subsubcontract dispute to the *Adjudicator* at the same time as the subcontract submission. The *Adjudicator* then settles the two disputes together and references to the Parties for the purposes of the dispute are interpreted as including the Subsubcontractor.

91.3 Where a matter disputed under or in connection with this subcontract is also a matter disputed under or in connection with the main contract, the *Contractor* may, by notifying the *Subcontractor*

- submit the subcontract dispute to the *main contract Adjudicator* at the same time as the main contract submission, this notification being within two weeks of the notification of the dispute by the *Subcontractor* to the *Contractor* and
- instruct the *Subcontractor* to provide any information which the *Contractor* may require.

The *main contract Adjudicator* then settles the two disputes together and references in the main contract to the Parties for the purpose of the disputes are interpreted as including the *Subcontractor*.

The *Adjudicator* **92**

92.1 The *Adjudicator* settles the dispute as independent adjudicator and not as arbitrator. His decision is enforceable as a matter of contractual obligation between the Parties and not as an arbitral award. The *Adjudicator*'s powers include the power to review and revise any action or inaction of the *Contractor* related to the dispute. Any communication between a Party and the *Adjudicator* is communicated also to the other Party. If the *Adjudicator*'s decision includes assessment of additional cost or delay caused to the *Subcontractor*, he makes his assessment in the same way as a compensation event is assessed.

92.2 If the *Adjudicator* resigns or is unable to act, the Parties choose a new adjudicator jointly. If the Parties have not chosen a new adjudicator jointly within four weeks of the *Adjudicator* resigning or becoming unable to act, a Party may ask the person stated in the Contract Data to choose a new adjudicator and the parties accept his choice. The new adjudicator is appointed as *Adjudicator* under the NEC Adjudicator's Contract. He has power to settle disputes that were currently submitted to his predecessor but had not been settled at the time when his predecessor resigned or became unable to act. The date of his appointment is the date of submission of these disputes to him as *Adjudicator*.

Review by the *tribunal* **93**

93.1 If after the *Adjudicator*

- notifies his decision or
- fails to do so

within the time provided by this subcontract a Party is dissatisfied, that Party notifies the other Party of his intention to refer the matter which he disputes to the *tribunal*. It is not referable to the *tribunal* unless the dissatisfied Party notifies his intention within three weeks of

- notification of the *Adjudicator*'s decision or
- the time provided by this subcontract for this notification if the *Adjudicator* fails to notify his decision within that time,

whichever is the earlier. The *tribunal* proceedings are not started before Completion of the whole of the *subcontract works* or earlier termination.

93.2　Where a subcontract dispute has been submitted together with the main contract submission to the *main contract Adjudicator*, and if after the *main contract Adjudicator*

- notifies his decision or
- fails to do so

within the time provided by the main contract a Party is dissatisfied, that Party notifies the other Parties of his intention to refer the matter which he disputes to the *main contract tribunal*. It is not referable to the *main contract tribunal* unless the dissatisfied Party notifies his intention within four weeks of

- notification of the *main contract Adjudicator*'s decision or
- the time provided by the main contract for this notification if the *main contract Adjudicator* fails to notify his decision within that time,

whichever is the earlier. The *main contract tribunal* proceedings are not started before Completion of the whole of the *works* or earlier termination of the main contract.

93.3　The *tribunal* settles the dispute referred to it. Its powers include the power to review and revise any decision of the *Adjudicator* and any action or inaction of the *Contractor* related to the dispute. A Party is not limited in the *tribunal* proceedings to the information, evidence or arguments put to the *Adjudicator*.

Termination　94

94.1　If either Party wishes to terminate he notifies the other Party giving details of his reason for terminating. The *Contractor* issues a termination certificate promptly if the reason complies with this subcontract.

94.2　The *Subcontractor* may terminate only for a reason identified in the Termination Table. The *Contractor* may terminate for any reason. The procedures followed and the amounts due on termination are in accordance with the Termination Table.

TERMINATION TABLE

Terminating Party	Reason	Procedure	Amount due
The *Contractor*	A reason other than R1 – R21	P1 and P2	A1, A2 and A4
	R1 – R15, R19	P1, P2 and P3	A1 and A3
	R17, R18, R21	P1 and P3	A1, A2 and A5
The *Subcontractor*	R1 – R10, R16, R20	P1 and P4	A1, A2 and A4
	R17, R18, R21	P1 and P4	A1, A2 and A5

94.3　The procedures for termination are implemented immediately after the *Contractor* has issued a termination certificate.

94.4　Within thirteen weeks of termination, the *Contractor* certifies a final payment to or from the *Subcontractor* which is the *Contractor*'s assessment of the amount due on termination less the total of previous payments.

94.5   After a termination certificate has been issued, the *Subcontractor* does no further work necessary to complete the *subcontract works*.

Reasons for termination   **95**

95.1   Either Party may terminate if the other Party has done one of the following or its equivalent

(a) If the other Party is an individual and has

- presented his petition for bankruptcy (R1),
- had a bankruptcy order made against him (R2),
- had a receiver appointed over his assets (R3) or
- made an arrangement with his creditors (R4).

(b) If the other Party is a company or partnership and has

- had a winding-up order made against it (R5),
- had a provisional liquidator appointed to it (R6),
- passed a resolution for winding-up (other than in order to amalgamate or reconstruct) (R9),
- had an administration order made against it (R8),
- had a receiver, receiver and manager, or administrative receiver appointed over the whole or a substantial part of its undertaking or assets (R7) or
- made an arrangement with its creditors (R10).

95.2   The *Contractor* may terminate if he has notified that the *Subcontractor* has defaulted in one of the following ways and not put the default right within three weeks of the notification.

- Substantially failed to comply with his obligations (R11).
- Not provided a bond or guarantee which this subcontract requires (R12).
- Appointed a Subsubcontractor for substantial work before the *Contractor* has accepted the Subsubcontractor (R13).

95.3   The *Contractor* may terminate if he has notified that the *Subcontractor* has defaulted in one of the following ways and not stopped defaulting within three weeks of the notification.

- Substantially hindered the *Employer*, the *Contractor* or Others (R14).
- Substantially broken a health or safety regulation (R15).

95.4   The *Subcontractor* may terminate if the *Contractor* has not paid an amount he has certified within thirteen weeks of the date of the certificate (R16).

95.5   Either Party may terminate if

- war or radioactive contamination has substantially affected the *Subcontractor*'s work for 26 weeks (R17) or
- the Parties have been released under the law from further performance of the whole of this subcontract (R18).

95.6   If the *Contractor* has instructed the *Subcontractor* to stop or not to start any substantial work or all work and an instruction allowing the work to restart or start has not been given within thirteen weeks,

- the *Contractor* may terminate if the instruction was due to a default by the *Subcontractor* (R19)
- the *Subcontractor* may terminate if the instruction was due to a default by the *Contractor* (R20) and
- either Party may terminate if the instruction was due to any other reason (R21).

Procedures on termination 96

96.1 On termination, the *Contractor* may complete the *subcontract works* himself or employ other people to do so and may use any Plant and Materials to which he has title (P1).

96.2 The procedure on termination also includes one or more of the following as set out in the Termination Table.

P2 The *Contractor* may instruct the *Subcontractor* to leave the Site, remove any Equipment, Plant and Materials from the Site and assign the benefit of any subsubcontract or other contract related to performance of this subcontract to the *Contractor*.

P3 The *Contractor* may use any Equipment to which he has title.

P4 The *Subcontractor* leaves the Working Areas and removes the Equipment.

Payment on termination 97

97.1 The amount due on termination includes (A1)

- an amount due assessed as for normal payments,
- the Actual Cost for Plant and Materials

  - within the Working Areas or
  - to which the *Contractor* has title and of which the *Subcontractor* has to accept delivery,

- other Actual Cost reasonably incurred in expectation of completing the whole of the *subcontract works*,
- any amounts retained by the *Contractor* and
- a deduction of any unrepaid balance of an advanced payment.

97.2 The amount due on termination also includes one or more of the following as set out in the Termination Table.

A2 The forecast Actual Cost of removing the Equipment.

A3 A deduction of the forecast of the additional cost to the *Contractor* of completing the whole of the *subcontract works*.

A4 The *fee percentage* applied to

- for Options A, B, C and D, any excess of the total of the Prices at the Subcontract Date over the Price for Work Done to Date or
- for Option E any excess of the first forecast of the Actual Cost for the *subcontract works* over the Price for Work Done to Date less the Fee.

A5 Half of A4.

MAIN OPTION CLAUSES

Option A: Priced subcontract with activity schedule

Identified and defined terms **11**

11.2 (20) The Prices are the lump sum prices for each of the activities in the *activity schedule* unless later changed in accordance with this subcontract.

(24) The Price for Work Done to Date is the total of the Prices for

- each group of completed activities and
- each completed activity which is not in a group

which is without Defects which would either delay or be covered by immediately following work.

(28) Actual Cost is the cost of the components in the Schedule of Cost Components whether work is subsubcontracted or not, excluding the cost of preparing quotations for compensation events.

The programme **31**

31.4 The *Subcontractor* shows the start and finish of each activity on the *activity schedule* on each programme which he submits for acceptance.

Acceleration **36**

36.3 When the *Contractor* accepts a quotation for an acceleration, he changes the Subcontract Completion Date and the Prices accordingly and accepts the revised programme.

The *activity schedule* **54**

54.1 Information in the *activity schedule* is not Subcontract Works Information or Site Information.

54.2 If the *Subcontractor* changes a planned method of working at his discretion so that the *activity schedule* does not comply with the Accepted Programme, he submits a revision of the *activity schedule* to the *Contractor* for acceptance.

54.3 A reason for not accepting a revision of the *activity schedule* is that

- it does not comply with the Accepted Programme,
- any changed Prices are not reasonably distributed between the activities or
- the total of the Prices is changed.

Assessing compensation events **63**

63.8 Assessments for changed Prices for compensation events are in the form of changes to the *activity schedule*.

63.10 The assessment of a compensation event which is or includes subsubcontracted work has the *Subcontractor's fee percentage* added to Actual Cost but fees paid or to be paid by the *Subcontractor* to the Subsubcontractor are not added.

63.11 If the *Contractor* and the *Subcontractor* agree, the *Subcontractor* assesses a compensation event using the Shorter Schedule of Cost Components. The *Contractor* may make his own assessments using the Shorter Schedule of Cost Components.

Implementing **65**
compensation events 65.4   The *Contractor* includes the changes to the Prices and the Subcontract Completion Date from the quotation which he has accepted or from his own assessment in his notification implementing a compensation event.

Payment on termination **97**   The amount due on termination is assessed without taking grouping of activities
97.3   into account.

Option B: Priced subcontract with bill of quantities

Identified and defined terms **11**

11.2 (21) The Prices are the lump sums and the amounts obtained by multiplying the rates by the quantities for the items in the *bill of quantities* unless later changed in accordance with this subcontract.

(25) The Price for Work Done to Date is the total of

- the quantity of the work which the *Subcontractor* has completed for each item in the *bill of quantities* multiplied by the rate and
- a proportion of each lump sum which is the proportion of the work covered by the item which the *Subcontractor* has completed.

In this clause, completed work means work without Defects which would either delay or be covered by immediately following work.

(28) Actual Cost is the cost of the components in the Schedule of Cost Components whether work is subsubcontracted or not excluding the cost of preparing quotations for compensation events.

Acceleration **36**

36.3 When the *Contractor* accepts a quotation for an acceleration, he changes the Subcontract Completion Date and the Prices accordingly and accepts the revised programme.

The *bill of quantities* **55**

55.1 Information in the *bill of quantities* is not Subcontract Works Information or Site Information.

Compensation events **60**

60.4 A difference between the final total quantity of work done and the quantity stated for an item in the *bill of quantities* at the Subcontract Date is a compensation event if

- the difference causes the Actual Cost per unit of quantity to change and
- the rate in the *bill of quantities* for the item at the Subcontract Date multiplied by the final total quantity of work done is more than 0.1% of the total of the Prices at the Subcontract Date.

If the Actual Cost per unit of quantity is reduced, the affected rate is reduced.

60.5 A difference between the final total quantity of work done and the quantity for an item stated in the *bill of quantities* at the Subcontract Date which delays Completion is a compensation event.

60.6 The *Contractor* corrects mistakes in the *bill of quantities* which are departures from the *method of measurement* or are due to ambiguities or inconsistencies. Each such correction is a compensation event which may lead to reduced Prices.

Assessing compensation events **63**

63.9 Assessments for changed Prices for compensation events are in the form of changes to the *bill of quantities*. If the *Contractor* and the *Subcontractor* agree, rates and lump sums in the *bill of quantities* may be used as a basis for assessment instead of Actual Cost and the resulting Fee.

63.10 The assessment of a compensation event which is or includes subsubcontracted work has the *Subcontractor's fee percentage* added to Actual Cost but fees paid or to be paid by the *Subcontractor* to the Subsubcontractor are not added.

63.11   If the *Contractor* and the *Subcontractor* agree, the *Subcontractor* assesses a compensation event using the Shorter Schedule of Cost Components. The *Contractor* may make his own assessments using the Shorter Schedule of Cost Components.

Implementing 65
compensation events

65.4   The *Contractor* includes the changes to the Prices and the Subcontract Completion Date from the quotation which he has accepted or from his own assessment in his notification implementing a compensation event.

Option C: Target subcontract with activity schedule

Identified and defined terms   **11**
  11.2

(20) The Prices are the lump sum prices for each of the activities in the *activity schedule* unless later changed in accordance with this subcontract.

(23) The Price for Work Done to Date is the Actual Cost which the *Subcontractor* has paid plus the Fee.

(27) Actual Cost is the amount of payments due to Subsubcontractors for work which is subsubcontracted and the cost of the components in the Schedule of Cost Components for work which is not subsubcontracted, less any Disallowed Cost.

(30) Disallowed Cost is cost which the *Contractor* decides

- is not justified by the *Subcontractor*'s accounts and records,
- should not have been paid to a Subsubcontractor in accordance with his subsubcontract,
- was incurred only because the *Subcontractor* did not

  - follow an acceptance or procurement procedure stated in the Subcontract Works Information or
  - give an early warning which he could have given or

- results from paying a Subsubcontractor more for a compensation event than is included in the accepted quotation or assessment for the compensation event

and the cost of

- correcting Defects after Completion,
- correcting Defects caused by the *Subcontractor* not complying with a requirement for how he is to Provide the Subcontract Works stated in the Subcontract Works Information,
- Plant and Materials not used to Provide the Subcontract Works (after allowing for reasonable wastage) and
- resources not used to Provide the Subcontract Works (after allowing for reasonable availability and utilisation) or not taken away from the Working Areas when the *Contractor* requested.

Providing the Subcontract Works   **20**
  20.3

The *Subcontractor* advises the *Contractor* on the practical implications of the design of the *subcontract works* and on subsubcontracting arrangements.

  20.4

The *Subcontractor* prepares forecasts of the total Actual Cost for the whole of the *subcontract works* in consultation with the *Contractor* and submits them to the *Contractor*. Forecasts are prepared at the intervals stated in the Subcontract Data from the *subcontract starting date* until Completion of the whole of the *subcontract works*. An explanation of the changes made since the previous forecast is submitted with each forecast.

Subsubcontracting   **26**
  26.4

The *Subcontractor* submits the proposed contract data for each subsubcontract for acceptance to the *Contractor* if

- the NEC Engineering and Construction Subcontract or the NEC Professional Services Contract is to be used and
- the *Contractor* instructs the *Subcontractor* to make the submission.

A reason for not accepting the proposed contract data is that its use will not allow the *Subcontractor* to Provide the Subcontract Works.

The programme 31

31.4   The *Subcontractor* shows the start and finish of each activity on the *activity schedule* on each programme which he submits for acceptance.

Acceleration 36

36.3   When the *Contractor* accepts a quotation for an acceleration, he changes the Subcontract Completion Date and the Prices accordingly and accepts the revised programme.

36.5   The *Subcontractor* submits a Subsubcontractor's proposal to accelerate to the *Contractor* for acceptance.

Assessing the amount due 50

50.6   Payments of Actual Cost made by the *Subcontractor* in a currency other than the *currency of this subcontract* are included in the amount due as payments to be made to him in the same currency. Such payments are converted to the *currency of this subcontract* in order to calculate the Fee and any *Subcontractor*'s share using the *exchange rates*.

Actual Cost 52

52.2   The *Subcontractor* keeps

- accounts of his payments of Actual Cost,
- records which show that the payments have been made,
- records of communications and calculations relating to assessment of compensation events for Subsubcontractors and
- other accounts and records as stated in the Subcontract Works Information.

52.3   The *Subcontractor* allows the *Contractor* to inspect at any time within working hours the accounts and records which he is required to keep.

The *Subcontractor*'s share 53

53.1   The *Contractor* assesses the *Subcontractor*'s share of the difference between the total of the Prices and the Price for Work Done to Date. The difference is divided into increments falling within each of the *share ranges*. The limits of a *share range* are a Price for Work Done to Date divided by the total of the Prices, expressed as a percentage. The *Subcontractor*'s share equals the sum of the products of the increment within each *share range* and the corresponding *Subcontractor*'s share percentage.

53.2   If the Price for Work Done to Date is less than the total of the Prices, the *Subcontractor* is paid his share of the saving. If the Price for Work Done to Date is greater than the total of the Prices, the *Subcontractor* pays his share of the excess.

53.3   The *Contractor* assesses the *Subcontractor*'s share at Completion of the whole of the *subcontract works* using his forecasts of the final Price for Work Done to Date and the final total of the Prices. This share is included in the amount due following Completion of the whole of the *subcontract works*.

53.4   The *Contractor* again assesses the *Subcontractor*'s share using the final Price for Work Done to Date and the final total of the Prices. This share is included in the final amount due.

53.5   If the *Contractor* accepts a proposal by the *Subcontractor* to change the Subcontract Works Information provided by the *Contractor* so that the Actual Cost is reduced, the Prices are not reduced.

The *activity schedule* **54**

54.1   Information in the *activity schedule* is not Subcontract Works Information or Site Information.

54.2   If the *Subcontractor* changes a planned method of working at his discretion so that the *activity schedule* does not comply with the Accepted Programme, he submits a revision of the *activity schedule* to the *Contractor* for acceptance.

54.3   A reason for not accepting a revision of the *activity schedule* is that

- it does not comply with the Accepted Programme,
- any changed Prices are not reasonably distributed between the activities or
- the total of the Prices is changed.

Assessing compensation events **63**

63.8   Assessments for changed Prices for compensation events are in the form of changes to the *activity schedule*.

63.11   If the *Contractor* and the *Subcontractor* agree, the *Subcontractor* assesses a compensation event using the Shorter Schedule of Cost Components. The *Contractor* may make his own assessments using the Shorter Schedule of Cost Components.

Implementing compensation events **65**

65.4   The *Contractor* includes the changes to the Prices and the Completion Date from the quotation which he has accepted or from his own assessment in his notification implementing a compensation event.

Payment on termination **97**

97.4   If there is a termination, the *Contractor* assesses the *Subcontractor*'s share after he has certified termination. His assessment uses the Price for Work Done to Date at termination and the total of the Prices for the work done before termination.

Option D: Target subcontract with bill of quantities

Identified and defined **11**
terms

11.2 (21) The Prices are the lump sums and the amounts obtained by multiplying the rates by the quantities for the items in the *bill of quantities* unless later changed in accordance with this subcontract.

(23) The Price for Work Done to Date is the Actual Cost which the *Subcontractor* has paid plus the Fee.

(27) Actual Cost is the amount of payments due to Subsubcontractors for work which is subsubcontracted and the cost of the components in the Schedule of Cost Components for work which is not subsubcontracted, less any Disallowed Cost.

(30) Disallowed Cost is cost which the *Contractor* decides

- is not justified by the *Subcontractor*'s accounts and records,
- should not have been paid to a Subsubcontractor in accordance with his subsubcontract,
- was incurred only because the *Subcontractor* did not

  - follow an acceptance or procurement procedure stated in the Subcontract Works Information or
  - give an early warning which he could have given or

- results from paying a Subsubcontractor more for a compensation event than is included in the accepted quotation or assessment for the compensation event

and the cost of

- correcting Defects after Completion,
- correcting Defects caused by the *Subcontractor* not complying with a requirement for how he is to Provide the Subcontract Works stated in the Subcontract Works Information,
- Plant and Materials not used to Provide the Subcontract Works (after allowing for reasonable wastage) and
- resources not used to Provide the Subcontract Works (after allowing for reasonable availability and utilisation) or not taken away from the Working Areas when the *Contractor* requested.

Providing the Subcontract **20**
Works

20.3 The *Subcontractor* advises the *Contractor* on the practical implications of the design of the subcontract works and on subsubcontracting arrangements.

20.4 The *Subcontractor* prepares forecasts of the total Actual Cost for the whole of the *subcontract works* in consultation with the *Contractor* and submits them to the *Contractor*. Forecasts are prepared at the intervals stated in the Subcontract Data from the *subcontract starting date* until Completion of the whole of the *subcontract works*. An explanation of the changes made since the previous forecast is submitted with each forecast.

Subsubcontracting **26**

26.4 The *Subcontractor* submits the proposed contract data for each subsubcontract for acceptance to the *Contractor* if

- the NEC Engineering and Construction Subcontract or the NEC Professional Services Contract is to be used and
- the *Contractor* instructs the *Subcontractor* to make the submission.

A reason for not accepting the proposed contract data is that its use will not allow the *Subcontractor* to Provide the Subcontract Works.

Acceleration **36**

36.3 When the *Contractor* accepts a quotation for an acceleration, he changes the Subcontract Completion Date and the Prices accordingly and accepts the revised programme.

36.5 The *Subcontractor* submits a Subsubcontractor's proposal to accelerate to the *Contractor* for acceptance.

Assessing the amount due **50**

50.6 Payments of Actual Cost made by the *Subcontractor* in a currency other than the *currency of this subcontract* are included in the amount due as payments to be made to him in the same currency. Such payments are converted to the *currency of this subcontract* in order to calculate the Fee and any *Subcontractor*'s share using the *exchange rates*.

Actual Cost **52**

52.2 The *Subcontractor* keeps

- accounts of his payments of Actual Cost,
- records which show that the payments have been made,
- records of communications and calculations relating to assessment of compensation events for Subsubcontractors and
- other accounts and records as stated in the Subcontract Works Information.

52.3 The *Subcontractor* allows the *Contractor* to inspect at any time within working hours the accounts and records which he is required to keep.

The *Subcontractor*'s share **53**

53.1 The *Contractor* assesses the *Subcontractor*'s share of the difference between the total of the Prices and the Price for Work Done to Date. The difference is divided into increments falling within each of the *share ranges*. The limits of a *share range* are a Price for Work Done to Date divided by the total of the Prices, expressed as a percentage. The *Subcontractor*'s share equals the sum of the products of the increment within each *share range* and the corresponding *Subcontractor's share percentage*.

53.2 If the Price for Work Done to Date is less than the total of the Prices, the *Subcontractor* is paid his share of the saving. If the Price for Work Done to Date is greater than the total of the Prices, the *Subcontractor* pays his share of the excess.

53.3 The *Contractor* assesses the *Subcontractor*'s share at Completion of the whole of the *subcontract works* using his forecasts of the final Price for Work Done to Date and the final total of the Prices. This share is included in the amount due following Completion of the whole of the *subcontract works*.

53.4 The *Contractor* again assesses the *Subcontractor*'s share using the final Price for Work Done to Date and the final total of the Prices. This share is included in the final amount due.

53.5 If the *Contractor* accepts a proposal by the *Subcontractor* to change the Subcontract Works Information provided by the *Contractor* which will reduce Actual Cost, the Prices are not reduced.

The *bill of quantities* 55

55.1 Information in the *bill of quantities* is not Subcontract Works Information or Site Information.

Compensation events 60

60.4 A difference between the final total quantity of work done and a quantity for an item stated in the *bill of quantities* at the Subcontract Date is a compensation event if

- the difference causes the Actual Cost per unit of quantity to change and
- the rate in the *bill of quantities* for the item at the Subcontract Date multiplied by the final total quantity of work done is more than 0.1% of the total of the Prices at the Subcontract Date.

If the Actual Cost per unit of quantity is reduced, the affected rate is reduced.

60.5 A difference between the final total quantity of work done and the quantity for an item stated in the *bill of quantities* at the Subcontract Date which delays Completion is a compensation event.

60.6 The *Contractor* corrects mistakes in the *bill of quantities* which are departures from the *method of measurement* or are due to ambiguities or inconsistencies. Each such correction is a compensation event which may lead to reduced Prices.

Assessing compensation 63
events 63.9 Assessments for changed Prices for compensation events are in the form of changes to the *bill of quantities*. If the *Contractor* and the *Subcontractor* agree, rates and lump sums in the *bill of quantities* may be used as a basis for assessment instead of Actual Cost and the resulting Fee.

63.11 If the *Contractor* and the *Subcontractor* agree, the *Subcontractor* assesses a compensation event using the Shorter Schedule of Cost Components. The *Contractor* may make his own assessments using the Shorter Schedule of Cost Components.

Implementing 65
compensation events 65.4 The *Contractor* includes the changes to the Prices and the Subcontract Completion Date from the quotation which he has accepted or from his own assessment in his notification implementing a compensation event.

Payment on termination 97

97.4 If there is a termination, the *Contractor* assesses the *Subcontractor*'s share after he has certified termination. His assessment uses the Price for Work Done to Date at termination and the total of the Prices for the work done before termination.

Option E: Cost reimbursable subcontract

Identified and defined	**11**	
terms	11.2	(19) The Prices are the Actual Cost plus the Fee.

(23) The Price for Work Done to Date is the Actual Cost which the *Subcontractor* has paid plus the Fee.

(27) Actual Cost is the amount of payments due to Subsubcontractors for work which is subsubcontracted and the cost of the components in the Schedule of Cost Components for work which is not subsubcontracted, less any Disallowed Cost.

(30) Disallowed Cost is cost which the *Contractor* decides

- is not justified by the *Subcontractor*'s accounts and records,
- should not have been paid to a Subsubcontractor in accordance with his subsubcontract,
- was incurred only because the *Subcontractor* did not

  - follow an acceptance or procurement procedure stated in the Subcontract Works Information or
  - give an early warning which he could have given or

- results from paying a Subsubcontractor more for a compensation event than is included in the accepted quotation or assessment for the compensation event

and the cost of

- correcting Defects after Completion,
- correcting Defects caused by the *Subcontractor* not complying with a requirement for how he is to Provide the Subcontract Works stated in the Subcontract Works Information,
- Plant and Materials not used to Provide the Subcontract Works (after allowing for reasonable wastage) and
- resources not used to Provide the Subcontract Works (after allowing for reasonable availability and utilisation) or not taken away from the Working Areas when the *Contractor* requested.

Providing the Subcontract	**20**	
Works	20.3	The *Subcontractor* advises the *Contractor* on the practical implications of the design of the *subcontract works* and on subsubcontracting arrangements.
	20.4	The *Subcontractor* prepares forecasts of the total Actual Cost for the whole of the *subcontract works* in consultation with the *Contractor* and submits them to the *Contractor*. Forecasts are prepared at the intervals stated in the Subcontract Data from the *subcontract starting date* until Completion of the whole of the *subcontract works*. An explanation of the changes made since the previous forecast is submitted with each forecast.

Subsubcontracting	**26**	
	26.4	The *Subcontractor* submits the proposed contract data for each subsubcontract for acceptance to the *Contractor* if

- the NEC Engineering and Construction Subcontract or the NEC Professional Services Contract is to be used and
- the *Contractor* instructs the *Subcontractor* to make the submission.

A reason for not accepting the proposed contract data is that its use will not allow the *Subcontractor* to Provide the Subcontract Works.

Acceleration **36**

36.4 When the *Contractor* accepts a quotation for an acceleration, he changes the Subcontract Completion Date accordingly and accepts the revised programme.

36.5 The *Subcontractor* submits a Subsubcontractor's proposal to accelerate to the *Contractor* for acceptance.

Assessing the amount due **50**

50.7 Payments of Actual Cost made by the *Subcontractor* in a currency other than the *currency of this subcontract* are included in the amount due as payments to be made to him in the same currency. Such payments are converted to the *currency of this subcontract* in order to calculate the Fee at the *exchange rates*.

Actual Cost **52**

52.2 The *Subcontractor* keeps

- accounts of his payments of Actual Cost,
- records which show that the payments have been made,
- records of communications and calculations relating to assessment of compensation events for Subsubcontractors and
- other accounts and records as stated in the Subcontract Works Information.

52.3 The *Subcontractor* allows the *Contractor* to inspect at any time within working hours the accounts and records which he is required to keep.

Assessing compensation events **63**

63.11 If the *Contractor* and the *Subcontractor* agree, the *Subcontractor* assesses a compensation event using the Shorter Schedule of Cost Components. The *Contractor* may make his own assessments using the Shorter Schedule of Cost Components.

Implementing compensation events **65**

65.3 The *Contractor* includes the changes to the forecast amount of the Prices and the Subcontract Completion Date in his notification to the *Subcontractor* implementing a compensation event.

65.5 The *Subcontractor* does not implement a subsubcontract compensation event until it has been agreed by the *Contractor*.

SECONDARY OPTION CLAUSES

Option G : Performance bond

Performance bond **G1**

G1.1   The *Subcontractor* gives the *Contractor* a performance bond provided by a bank or insurer, which the *Contractor* has accepted for the amount stated in the Subcontract Data and in the form set out in the Subcontract Works Information. A reason for not accepting the bank or insurer is that its commercial position is not strong enough to carry the bond. If the bond was not given by the Subcontract Date, it is given to the *Contractor* within four weeks of the Subcontract Date.

Option H : Parent company guarantee

Parent company guarantee **H1**

H1.1   If a parent company owns the *Subcontractor*, the *Subcontractor* gives to the *Contractor* a guarantee by the parent company of the *Subcontractor*'s performance in the form set out in the Subcontract Works Information. If the guarantee was not given by the Subcontract Date, it is given to the *Contractor* within four weeks of the Subcontract Date.

Option J : Advanced payment to the *Subcontractor*

Advanced payment **J1**

J1.1   The *Contractor* makes an advanced payment to the *Subcontractor* of the amount stated in the Subcontract Data.

J1.2   The advanced payment is made either within five weeks of the Subcontract Date or, if an advanced payment bond is required, within four weeks of the later of

- the Subcontract Date
- the date when the *Contractor* receives the advanced payment bond.

The advanced payment bond is issued by a bank or insurer which the *Contractor* has accepted. A reason for not accepting the proposed bank or insurer is that its commercial position is not strong enough to carry the bond. The bond is for the amount of the advanced payment and in the form set out in the Subcontract Works Information. Delay in making the advanced payment is a compensation event.

J1.3   The advanced payment is repaid to the *Contractor* by the *Subcontractor* in instalments of the amount stated in the Subcontract Data. An instalment is included in each amount due assessed after the period stated in the Subcontract Data has passed until the advanced payment has been repaid.

Option K : Multiple currencies (used only with Options A and B)

Multiple currencies **K1**

K1.1   The *Subcontractor* is paid in currencies other than the *currency of this subcontract* for the work listed in the Subcontract Data. The *exchange rates* are used to convert from the *currency of this subcontract* to other currencies.

K1.2   Payments to the *Subcontractor* in currencies other than the *currency of this subcontract* do not exceed the maximum amounts stated in the Subcontract Data. Any excess is paid in the *currency of this subcontract.*

Option L : Sectional Completion

Sectional Completion **L1**

L1.1   In these *conditions of contract*, unless stated as the whole of the *subcontract works*, each reference and clause relevant to

- the *subcontract works*,
- Completion and
- Subcontract Completion Date

applies, as the case may be, to either the whole of the *subcontract works* or any *section* of the *subcontract works*.

Option M : Limitation of the *Subcontractor*'s liability for his design to reasonable skill and care

The *Subcontractor*'s **M1**
design   M1.1   The *Subcontractor* is not liable for Defects in the *subcontract works* due to his design so far as he proves that he used reasonable skill and care to ensure that it complied with the Subcontract Works Information.

Option N : Price adjustment for inflation (used only with Options A, B, C and D)

Defined terms **N1**

N1.1   (a) The Base Date Index (B) is the latest available index before the *base date.*

(b) The Latest Index (L) is the latest available index before the date of assessment of an amount due.

(c) The Price Adjustment Factor is the total of the products of each of the proportions stated in the Subcontract Data multiplied by (L - B)/B for the index linked to it.

Price Adjustment Factors N2

N2.1 If an index is changed after it has been used in calculating a Price Adjustment Factor, the calculation is repeated and a correction included in the next assessment of the amount due.

N2.2 The Price Adjustment Factor calculated at the Subcontract Completion Date for the whole of the *subcontract works* is used for calculating the price adjustment after this date.

Compensation events N3

N3.1 The Actual Cost for compensation events is assessed using the

- Actual Costs current at the time of assessing the compensation event adjusted to *base date* by dividing by one plus the Price Adjustment Factor for the last assessment of the amount due and
- Actual Costs at *base date* levels for amounts calculated from rates stated in the Subcontract Data for employees and Equipment.

Price adjustment N4

Options A and B N4.1 Each amount due includes an amount for price adjustment which is the sum of

- the change in the Price for Work Done to Date since the last assessment of the amount due multiplied by the Price Adjustment Factor for the date of the current assessment,
- the amount for price adjustment included in the previous amount due and
- correcting amounts, not included elsewhere, which arise from changes to indices used for assessing previous amounts for price adjustment.

Options C and D N4.2 Each time the amount due is assessed, an amount for price adjustment is added to the total of the Prices which is the sum of

- the change in the Price for Work Done to Date since the last assessment of the amount due multiplied by $(1 - 1/(1 + PAF))$ where PAF is the Price Adjustment Factor for the date of the current assessment and
- correcting amounts, not included elsewhere, which arise from changes to indices used for assessing previous amounts for price adjustment.

Option P : Retention

Retention P1

P1.1 After the Price for Work Done to Date has reached the *retention free amount*, an amount is retained in each amount due assessed. Until the earlier of

- Completion of the whole of the *subcontract works* and
- the date on which the *Contractor* takes over the whole of the *subcontract works*

the amount retained is the *retention percentage* applied to the excess of the Price for Work Done to Date above the *retention free amount*.

P1.2 The amount retained is halved

- in the assessment made at Completion of the whole of the *subcontract works* or
- in the next assessment after the *Contractor* has taken over the whole of the *subcontract works* if this is before Completion of the whole of the *subcontract works*.

The amount retained remains at this amount until the Defects Certificate is issued. No amount is retained in the assessments made after the Defects Certificate has been issued.

Option Q : Bonus for early Completion

Bonus for early Completion Q1

Q1.1 The *Subcontractor* is paid a bonus calculated at the rate stated in the Subcontract Data for each day from the earlier of

- Completion and
- the date on which the *Contractor* takes over the *subcontract works*

until the Subcontract Completion Date.

Option R : Delay damages

Delay damages R1

R1.1 The *Subcontractor* pays delay damages at the rate stated in the Subcontract Data from the Subcontract Completion Date for each day until the earlier of

- Completion and
- the date on which the *Contractor* takes over the *subcontract works*.

R1.2 If the Subcontract Completion Date is changed to a later date after delay damages have been paid, the *Contractor* repays the overpayment of damages with interest. Interest is assessed from the date of payment to the date of repayment and the date of repayment is an assessment date.

Option S : Low performance damages

Low performance damages S1

S1.1 If a Defect included in the Defects Certificate shows low performance with respect to a performance level stated in the Subcontract Data, the *Subcontractor* pays the amount of low performance damages stated in the Subcontract Data.

Option T : Changes in the law

Changes in the law   **T1**

      T1.1   A change in the law of the country in which the Site is located is a compensation event if it occurs after the Subcontract Date. The *Contractor* may notify the *Subcontractor* of a compensation event for a change in the law and instruct him to submit quotations. If the effect of a compensation event which is a change in the law is to reduce the total Actual Cost, the Prices are reduced.

Option U : The Construction (Design and Management) Regulations 1994 (to be used for contracts in UK)

The CDM Regulations   **U1**
1994   U1.1   A delay to the work or additional or changed work caused by application of The Construction (Design and Management) Regulations 1994 is a compensation event if an experienced contractor could not reasonably be expected to have foreseen it.

Option V : Trust Fund (used when Option V is used in the main contract)

Trust Fund   **V1**

      V1.1   The *Employer* has established a Trust Fund held and administered by the *Trustees*. The Trust Deed is a deed between the *Employer* and the *Trustees* which contains the provisions for administering the Trust Fund.

      V1.2   The *Contractor* informs the *Subcontractor* of the terms of the Trust Deed and of the appointment of the *Trustees*.

      V1.3   The *Subcontractor* informs his suppliers and subsubcontractors of the terms of the Trust Deed and of the appointment of the *Trustees*. He arranges that subsubcontractors ensure that their suppliers and subcontractors, of whatever tier, are also informed.

Option Z : Additional conditions of subcontract

Additional conditions of   **Z1**
subcontract   Z1.1   The additional conditions of subcontract stated in the Subcontract Data are part of this subcontract.

SCHEDULE OF COST COMPONENTS

When Option C, D or E is used, in this schedule the *Subcontractor* means the *Subcontractor* and not his Subsubcontractors. Amounts are included only in one cost component.

People **1** The following components of the cost of

- people who are directly employed by the *Subcontractor* and whose normal place of working is within the Working Areas,
- people who are directly employed by the *Subcontractor* and whose normal place of working is not within the Working Areas but who are working in the Working Areas for a period of not less than one week and
- people who are not directly employed by the *Subcontractor* but are paid by the *Subcontractor* according to the time worked whilst they are within the Working Areas.

11 Wages and salaries.

12 Payments to people for

(a) bonuses and incentives
(b) overtime
(c) working in special circumstances
(d) special allowances
(e) absence due to sickness and holidays
(f) severance related to work on this subcontract.

13 Payments made in relation to people for

(a) travelling to and from the Working Areas
(b) subsistence and lodging
(c) relocation
(d) medical examinations
(e) passports and visas
(f) travel insurance
(g) items (a) to (f) for a spouse or dependents
(h) protective clothing
(j) meeting the requirements of the law
(k) superannuation and life assurance
(l) death benefit
(m) occupational accident benefits
(n) medical aid.

Equipment **2** The following components of the cost of Equipment which is used within the Working Areas (excluding Equipment cost covered by the percentage for Working Areas overheads).

21 Payments for the hire of Equipment not owned by the *Subcontractor*, by the *Subcontractor*'s parent company or by another part of a group with the same parent company.

22 An amount for depreciation and maintenance of Equipment which is

(a) owned by the *Subcontractor*
(b) purchased by the *Subcontractor* under a hire purchase or lease agreement or
(c) hired by the *Subcontractor* from the *Subcontractor*'s parent company or another part of a group with the same parent company.

The depreciation and maintenance charge is the actual purchase price of the item of Equipment (or first cost if the *Subcontractor* assembled, fabricated or otherwise produced the item of Equipment) divided by its average working life remaining at the time of purchase, assembly or fabrication (expressed in weeks). First cost is limited to the cost of manufacture when the item of Equipment came into being.

The amount for depreciation and maintenance is calculated by multiplying the depreciation and maintenance charge by the time required and then increasing the product by the appropriate percentage for Equipment depreciation and maintenance stated in the Subcontract Data.

The time required is the number of weeks and part weeks. A part week is measured in half days and is expressed as one twelfth of a week. A part half day is taken as a half day. In the case of idle or standby time the first half day is deducted.

23 The purchase price of Equipment which is consumed.

24 Unless included in the hire rates or the depreciation and maintenance charge, payments for

> (a) transporting Equipment to and from the Working Areas
> (b) erecting and dismantling Equipment
> (c) upgrading or modification needed for a compensation event.

25 Unless included in the hire rates or the depreciation and maintenance charge, the cost of operatives is included in the cost of people.

Plant and Materials 3 The following components of the cost of Plant and Materials.

31 Payments for

> (a) purchasing Plant and Materials
> (b) delivery to and removal from the Working Areas
> (c) providing and removing packaging
> (d) samples and tests.

32 Cost is credited with payments received for disposal of Plant and Materials.

Charges 4 The following components of the cost of charges paid by the *Subcontractor*.

41 Payments to utilities for provision and use in the Working Areas of

> (a) water
> (b) gas
> (c) electricity
> (d) other services.

42 Payments to public authorities, utilities and other properly constituted authorities of charges which they are authorised to make in respect of the *subcontract works*.

43 Payments for

> (a) financing charges (excluding charges compensated for by interest paid in accordance with this subcontract)
> (b) buying or leasing land
> (c) compensation for loss of crops or buildings
> (d) royalties
> (e) inspection certificates
> (f) rent of premises in the Working Areas
> (g) charges for access to the Working Areas
> (h) facilities for visits to the Working Areas by Others
> (j) specialist services.

44   A charge for overhead costs incurred within the Working Areas calculated by applying the percentage for Working Areas overheads stated in the Subcontract Data to the total of people items 11, 12 and 13. The charge includes provision and use of accommodation, equipment, supplies and services for

(a) offices and drawing offices
(b) laboratories
(c) workshops
(d) stores and compounds
(e) labour camps
(f) cabins
(g) catering
(h) medical facilities and first aid
(j) recreation
(k) sanitation
(l) security
(m) copying
(n) telephone, telex, fax, radio and CCTV
(o) surveying and setting out
(p) computing
(q) hand tools and hand held powered tools.

Manufacture and fabrication   **5**   The following components of the cost of manufacture or fabrication of Plant and Materials which are

- wholly or partly designed specifically for the *subcontract works* and
- manufactured or fabricated outside the Working Areas.

51   The total of the hours worked by employees multiplied by the hourly rates stated in the Subcontract Data for the categories of employees listed.

52   An amount for overheads calculated by multiplying this total by the percentage for manufacturing and fabrication overheads stated in the Subcontract Data.

Design   **6**   The following components of the cost of design of the *subcontract works* and Equipment done outside the Working Areas.

61   The total of the hours worked by employees multiplied by the hourly rates stated in the Subcontract Data for the categories of employees listed.

62   An amount for overheads calculated by multiplying this total by the percentage for design overheads stated in the Subcontract Data.

63   The cost of travel to and from the Working Areas for the categories of employees listed in the Subcontract Data.

Insurance   **7**   The following are deducted from cost:

- costs against which this subcontract requires the *Subcontractor* to insure and
- other costs paid to the *Subcontractor* by insurers.

SHORTER SCHEDULE OF COST COMPONENTS

When Option C, D or E is used, in this schedule the *Subcontractor* means the *Subcontractor* and not his Subsubcontractors. Amounts are included only in one cost component.

People 1 The following components of the cost of

- people who are directly employed by the *Subcontractor* and whose normal place of working is within the Working Areas and
- people who are directly employed by the *Subcontractor* and whose normal place of working is not within the Working Areas but who are working in the Working Areas for a period of not less than one week and
- people who are not directly employed by the *Subcontractor* but are paid by the *Subcontractor* according to the time worked whilst they are within the Working Areas.

11 Wages and salaries.

12 Payments to people for

(a) bonuses and incentives
(b) overtime
(c) working in special circumstances
(d) special allowances.

13 Payments made in relation to people for

(a) travelling to and from the Working Areas
(b) subsistence and lodging.

Equipment 2 The following components of the cost of Equipment used within the Working Areas (excluding Equipment cost covered by the percentage for people overheads).

21 Amounts for Equipment which is in the published list stated in the Subcontract Data. These amounts are calculated by applying the percentage adjustment for listed Equipment stated in the Subcontract Data to the rates in the published list and by multiplying the resulting rate by the time for which the Equipment is required.

22 Amounts for Equipment listed in the Subcontract Data which is not in the published list stated in the Subcontract Data. These amounts are the rates stated in the Subcontract Data multiplied by the time for which the Equipment is required.

23 The time required is expressed as hours, days, weeks or months consistent with the list of items of Equipment in the Subcontract Data or the published list stated in the Subcontract Data. For idle and standby time, the following times are deducted:

- the first two hours for items paid at an hourly rate,
- the first half day for items paid at a daily rate,
- the first third of a week for items paid at a weekly rate and
- the first quarter of a month for items paid at a monthly rate.

24 Unless the item is in the published list and the rate includes the cost component, payments for

(a) transporting Equipment to and from the Working Areas
(b) erecting and dismantling Equipment
(c) upgrading or modification needed for a compensation event.

25 Unless the item is in the published list and the rate includes the cost component, the purchase price of Equipment which is consumed.

	26	Unless the item is in the published list and the rate includes the cost component, the cost of operatives is included in the cost of people.
Plant and Materials	**3**	The following components of the cost of Plant and Materials.
	31	Payments for

(a) purchasing Plant and Materials
(b) delivery to and removal from the Working Areas
(c) providing and removing packaging
(d) samples and tests.

32   Cost is credited with payments received for disposal of Plant and Materials.

Charges   **4**   A charge calculated by applying the percentage for people overheads stated in the Subcontract Data to the total of people items 11, 12 and 13 to cover the costs of

(a) overhead payments for people including payroll burdens
(b) payments to utilities for the provision and use in the Working Areas of water, gas, electricity and other services
(c) payments to public authorities, utilities and other properly constituted authorities of charges which they are authorised to make in respect of the *subcontract works*
(d) payments for financing charges (excluding charges compensated for by interest paid in accordance with this subcontract), buying or leasing land, compensation for loss of crops or buildings, royalties, inspection certificates, rent of premises in the Working Areas, charges for access to the Working Areas, facilities for visits to the Working Areas by Others and specialist services
(e) payments for accommodation, equipment, supplies and services for offices, drawing office, laboratories, workshops, stores and compounds, labour camps, cabins, catering, medical facilities and first aid, recreation, sanitation, security, copying, telephone, telex, fax, radio, CCTV, surveying and setting out, computing, hand tools and hand held powered tools.

Manufacture and fabrication   **5**   The following components of the cost of manufacture or fabrication of Plant and Materials which are

- wholly or partly designed specifically for the *subcontract works* and
- manufactured or fabricated outside the Working Areas.

51   The total of the hours worked by employees multiplied by the hourly rates stated in the Subcontract Data for the categories of employees listed.

52   An amount for overheads calculated by multiplying this total by the percentage for manufacturing and fabrication overheads stated in the Subcontract Data.

Design   **6**   The following components of the cost of design of the *subcontract works* and Equipment done outside the Working Areas.

61   The total of the hours worked by employees multiplied by the hourly rates stated in the Subcontract Data for the categories of employees listed.

62   An amount for overheads calculated by multiplying this total by the percentage for design overheads stated in the Subcontract Data.

63   The cost of travel to and from the Working Areas for the categories of employees listed in the Subcontract Data.

Insurance   **7**   The following are deducted from cost:

- costs against which this subcontract requires the *Subcontractor* to insure and
- other costs paid to the *Subcontractor* by insurers.

SUBCONTRACT DATA

Part one – Data provided by the *Contractor*

Statements given in all subcontracts

1. General

- The *conditions of subcontract* are the core clauses and the clauses for Options . . . . of the second edition (1995) of the NEC Engineering and Construction Subcontract.

- The *works* in the main contract are

  . . . .

- The *subcontract works* are

  . . . .

- The *Contractor* is

  Name . . . .

  Address . . . .

  . . . .

- The *Employer* in the main contract is

  Name . . . .

  Address . . . .

  . . . .

- The *Project Manager* in the main contract is

  Name . . . .

  Address . . . .

  . . . .

- The *Supervisor* in the main contract is

  Name . . . .

  Address . . . .

  . . . .

- The *Adjudicator* in this subcontract is

  Name . . . .

  Address . . . .

  . . . .

- The *main contract Adjudicator* is

  Name . . . .

  Address . . . .

  . . . .

- The Subcontract Works Information is in

  . . . .

  . . . .

  . . . .

  . . . .

  . . . .

  . . . .

  . . . .

- The Site Information is in

  . . . .

  . . . .

  . . . .

  . . . .

  . . . .

  . . . .

  . . . .

- The *boundaries of the site* are . . . .

- The *language of this subcontract* is . . . .

- The *law of the subcontract* is the law of . . . .

- The *period for reply* to a communication is

  for a reply by the *Contractor*. . . . . .weeks

  for a reply by the *Subcontractor* .weeks

2. The *Subcontractor*'s main responsibilities

- The *Subcontractor*'s liability for Defects due to his design that are not listed on the Defects Certificate is limited to . . . .

  . . . .

3. Time

- The *subcontract starting date* is . . . .

- The *subcontract possession dates* are

Part of the Site	Date
1	. . . .
2	. . . .
3	. . . .

- The *Subcontractor* submits revised programmes at intervals no longer than

  . . . . weeks

4. Testing and Defects
- The *defects date* is . . . . weeks after Completion of the whole of the *subcontract works*

- The *defect correction period* is . . . . weeks

5. Payment
- The *currency of this subcontract* is the . . . .

- The *assessment interval* is . . . . weeks (not more than five)

- The *interest rate* is . . . . % per annum (not less than 2) above the . . . .

  rate of the . . . . bank

6. Compensation events
- The place where weather is to be recorded is

  . . . .

- The *weather measurements* to be recorded for each calendar month are
  - the cumulative rainfall (mm)
  - the number of days with rainfall more than 5 mm
  - the number of days with minimum air temperature less than 0 degrees Celsius
  - the number of days with snow lying at . . . . hours GMT

    and these measurements:

    . . . .

    . . . .

    . . . .

- The *weather data* are the records of past *weather measurements* for each calendar

  month which were recorded at . . . .

  and which are available from . . . .

  . . . .

Where no recorded data are available

- Assumed values for the ten year return *weather data* for each *weather measurement* for each calendar month are:

  . . . .

  . . . .

  . . . .

  . . . .

8. Risks and insurance
- The amount of the minimum limit of indemnity for insurance in respect of loss of or damage to property (except the *subcontract works*, Plant and Materials and Equipment) and liability for bodily injury to or death of a person (not an employee of the *Subcontractor*) due to activity in connection with this subcontract for any one event is

  . . . .

- The amount of the minimum limit of indemnity for insurance in respect of death of or bodily injury to employees of the *Subcontractor* arising out of and in the course of their employment in connection with this subcontract is . . . .

  . . . .

9. Disputes and termination

- The person who will choose a new adjudicator if the Parties cannot agree a choice is

  ....

- The *tribunal* is ....

- The *main contract tribunal* is ....

Optional statements

If the *tribunal* or the *main contract tribunal* is arbitration

- The arbitration procedure is..

If the *Contractor* has decided the *subcontract completion date* for the whole of the *subcontract works*

- The *subcontract completion date* for the whole of the *subcontract works* is ....

  ....

If the *Contractor* is not willing to take over the *subcontract works* before the Subcontract Completion Date

- The *Contractor* is not willing to take over the *subcontract works* before the Sub-contract Completion Date.

If no programme is identified in part two of the Subcontract Data

- The *Subcontractor* is to submit a first programme for acceptance within .... weeks of the Subcontract Date

If the period for payment is not four weeks

- The period within which payments are made is ....weeks

If there are additional compensation events

- These are compensation events

  1 ....

  2 ....

  3 ....

If there are additional *Employer*'s or *Contractor*'s risks

- These are additional *Employer*'s risks

  1 ....

  2 ....

  3 ....

- These are additional *Contractor*'s risks

  1 ....

  2 ....

  3 ....

If the *Employer* or *Contractor* is to provide Plant and Materials

- The insurance against loss of or damage to the *subcontract works*, Plant and Materials is to include cover for Plant and Materials provided by the *Employer* or *Contractor* for an amount of . . . .

If the *Employer* or *Contractor* is to provide any of the insurances stated in the Insurance Table

- The *Employer* or *Contractor* provides these insurances from the Insurance Table

  1. Insurance against . . . .

  Cover/indemnity is . . . .

  The deductibles are . . . .

  2. Insurance against . . . .

  Cover/indemnity is . . . .

  The deductibles are . . . .

  3. Insurance against . . . .

  Cover/indemnity is . . . .

  The deductibles are . . . .

If additional insurances are to be provided

- The *Employer* or *Contractor* provides these additional insurances

  1. Insurance against . . . .

  Cover/indemnity is . . . .

  The deductibles are . . . .

  2. Insurance against . . . .

  Cover/indemnity is . . . .

  The deductibles are . . . .

  3. Insurance against . . . .

  Cover/indemnity is . . . .

  The deductibles are . . . .

- The *Subcontractor* provides these additional insurances

  1. Insurance against . . . .

  Cover/indemnity is . . . .

  2. Insurance against . . . .

  Cover/indemnity is . . . .

  3. Insurance against . . . .

  Cover/indemnity is . . . .

If Option B or D is used

- The *method of measurement* is . . . .

  amended as follows . . . .

  . . . .

  . . . .

If Option C or D is used

- The *Subcontractor's share percentages* and the *share ranges* are

share range	*Subcontractor's share percentage*
less than . . . . %	. . . . %
from . . . . . . % to . . . . . . %	. . . . %
from . . . . . . % to . . . . . . %	. . . . %
greater than . . . . %	. . . . %

If Option C, D or E is used

- The *Subcontractor* prepares forcasts of Actual Cost for the *subcontract works* at

  intervals no longer than. . . . . weeks

- The *exchange rates* are those published in . . . .

  on . . . . (date)

If Option G is used

- The amount of the performance bond is . . . .

If Option J is used

- The amount of the advanced payment is . . . .

- The *Subcontractor* repays the instalments in assessments starting not less than

  . . . . weeks after the Subcontract Date.

- The instalments are . . . .

  . . . .

(either an amount or a percentage of the payment otherwise due)

- An advanced payment bond <u>is/is not</u> required

57

NEC ENGINEERING AND CONSTRUCTION SUBCONTRACT

If Option K is used

- The *Contractor* will pay for the items or activities listed below in the currencies stated

  Items and activities   Currency   Maximum payment

  ....

  ....

  ....

- The *exchange rates* are those published in ....

  on .... (date)

If Option L is used

- The *subcontract completion date* for each *section* of the *subcontract works* is

Section	Description	*Subcontract completion date*
1	....	....
2	....	....
3	....	....
4	....	....
5	....	....

If Options L and Q are used together

- The bonuses for the *section*s of the *subcontract works* are

Section	Description	Amount per day
1	....	....
2	....	....
3	....	....
4	....	....
5	....	....

If Options L and R are used together

- Delay damages for the *section*s of the *subcontract works* are

Section	Description	Amount per day
1	....	....
2	....	....
3	....	....
4	....	....
5	....	....

If Option N is used

- The proportions used to calculate the Price Adjustment Factor are

  0 · . . . .   linked to the index for . . . .

  0 · . . . .

  0 · . . . .

  0 · . . . .

  0 · . . . .

  0 · . . . .

  0 · . . . .   non-adjustable

  ─────────────

  1 · 00

- The *base date* for indices is . . . .

- The indices are those prepared by . . . .

If Option P is used

- The *retention free amount* is . . . .

- The *retention percentage* is . . . . %

If Option Q is used

- The bonus for the whole of the *subcontract works* is . . . . per day

If Option R is used (whether or not Option L is also used)

- Delay damages for the whole of the *subcontract works* are . . . . per day

If Option S is used

- The amounts for low performance damages are

Amount	Performance level
. . . .	for . . . .
. . . .	for . . . .
. . . .	for . . . .
. . . .	for . . . .

If Option V is used

- The *Trustees* are

  Name . . . .

  Address . . . .

  Name . . . .

  Address . . . .

If Option Z is used

- The additional conditions of subcontract are . . . .

  . . . .

Part two - Data provided by the *Subcontractor*

Statements given in all subcontracts

- The *Subcontractor* is

  Name . . . .

  Address . . . .

  . . . .

- The *fee percentage* is . . . . %

- The *working areas* are the Site and . . . .

- The key people are

  (1) Name . . . .

  Job . . . .

  Responsibilities . . . .

  . . . .

  Qualifications . . . .

  Experience . . . .

  . . . .

  (2) Name . . . .

  Job . . . .

  Responsibilities . . . .

  . . . .

  Qualifications . . . .

  Experience . . . .

  . . . .

Data for Schedule of Cost Components

- The hourly rates for Actual Cost of manufacture or fabrication outside the Working Areas are

Category of employee	Hourly rate
. . . .	. . . .
. . . .	. . . .
. . . .	. . . .
. . . .	. . . .

- The percentage for manufacture or fabrication overheads is . . . . %

- The hourly rates for Actual Cost of design outside the Working Areas are

Category of employee   Hourly rate

....

....

....

....

- The percentage for design overheads is .... %

- The categories of employees whose travelling expenses to and from the Working Areas are included in Actual Cost are

....

....

....

....

Not used with the Shorter Schedule of Cost Components

- Except for special items the percentage for Equipment depreciation and maintenance is .... %

- The percentages for depreciation and maintenance for special items of Equipment are:

Equipment   Size or capacity   %

....

....

....

....

- The percentage for Working Areas overheads is .... %

Only used with the Shorter Schedule of Cost Components

- The percentage for people overheads is .... %

- The published list of Equipment is the last edition of the list published by

....

- The percentage for adjustment for listed Equipment is .... %

- The rates of other Equipment are

Equipment   Size or capacity   Rate

....

....

....

....

Optional statements   **If the *Subcontractor* is to provide Subcontract Works Information for his design**

- The Subcontract Works Information for the *Subcontractor*'s design is in

....

....

....

....

....

....

If a programme is to be identified in the Subcontract Data

- The programme identified in the Subcontract Data is............................

....

If the *Subcontractor* is to decide the *subcontract completion date* for the whole of the *subcontract works*

- The *subcontract completion date* for the whole of the *subcontract works* is ....

If Option A or C is used

- The *activity schedule* is ....

If Option B or D is used

- The *bill of quantities* is ....

If Option A, B, C or D is used

- The tendered total of the Prices is ....

NEC ENGINEERING AND CONSTRUCTION SUBCONTRACT

Index by clause numbers (option clauses are indicated by their letters)